ABOUT THIS BOOK

SUBJECT MATTER

This book is an introduction to the techniques and skills of writing stories, essays and compositions in English. In addition to this primary purpose, it is also designed to help in the development of vocabulary, sentence construction and comprehension skills. A great deal of information has deliberately been included, in a concise but readable form, and using formal terminology where appropriate.

This book is intended to help the children using it to write their own language. It should also help them to understand how others use that language. But above all the aim is that they should develop their own powers to write good English to good effect.

LAYOUT

The format is that of a (re-usable) workbook. Each double page provides a factsheet on a particular topic facing a worksheet designed to test the knowledge or skill provided, to help the child to understand its application, and to give practice in its use. Putting factsheet and worksheet together is intended to make reference back very simple. Testsheets to monitor progress are provided at the end of the book, together with a list of composition topics and an index.

USE

The factsheets can be used directly by the pupil as an information source. Alternatively they can be used to provide the basis of the teaching content of a lesson, or as reinforcement of the teacher's own lesson plans and schemes of work.

The worksheets are intended to be used by pupils working alone or in groups, with support and assistance available from the teacher, or from parents.

The book can readily be used for work done at home.

A suggested marking scheme is provided for each exercise and worksheet, with a total of 2,400 marks for the twenty-eight worksheets and a further 600 for the testsheets. Teachers may, of course, wish to vary the weightings given to exercises, or to employ their own systems of marking. However, it is envisaged that the marking of the worksheets *with* the pupils who have done them will in itself provide a useful teaching vehicle.

AGE/ABILITY RANGE

The content of this book has been tested with pupils as young as ten and as old as fifteen, with a remarkable degree of success.

More or less support will, of course, be required from the teacher depending on the age and ability of the children using the book.

It is best suited to pupils in secondary schools and those in the upper forms of preparatory and middle schools, in the age range of 11+ to 14+, and of average or above average ability.

It is not essential to have used the first two books in the *Help Yourself to English* series to be able to work from this book, though it can be used very conveniently in conjunction with the preceding and subsequent titles in the course.

A reading age of 11+ is recommended, and the book would not generally be suitable for remedial teaching groups. It may, however, readily be employed as a revision primer for older pupils, particularly those taking public examinations.

FACTSHEET ONE

SYNONYMS (1) — VARIETY

Variety is the spice of life!
Look at this passage from a novel:—

> I glanced up at his implacable face, looking for some sympathy there, but his eyes were like steel in that ruthless visage. The countenance I beheld was that of an ancient, vengeful deity, devoid of compassion. I could expect no pity from such as he.

Leaving aside the question of what you may think of this sort of writing, you probably did *not* notice while you were reading it that the writer uses three different words for 'face':— *face* itself, *visage* and *countenance*. These three words are SYNONYMS. Synonyms are words that *mean the same* as each other. Here is a short list of synonyms to give you the idea:—

start, begin, commence	brave, daring, courageous, intrepid
conclude, end, finish, terminate	far, distant, remote
see, observe, watch, notice	annoyed, angry, furious, irate
pain, suffering, torment, anguish	sky, heavens, firmament, atmosphere.

The fact is that very many words in English do have synonyms. The exceptions are:—

(a) Common nouns standing for specific objects, like *bookcase, banana, elephant, bus;*
(b) A smaller number of verbs indicating specific actions, like *kick, point, yawn, dress;*
(c) The little words that hold sentences together:— pronouns (*he, she, it, me, us, mine, yours* etc); prepositions (*on, in, at, by, with, from, to, for* etc.); conjunctions (*and, but, if, so, or* etc.); and the three articles (*a, an, the*).

Look back at the short passage we started with for a moment. There seem to be other examples of synonyms in it. What about *glanced, looking, beheld*? The three verbs, 'to look', 'to glance' and 'to behold' all mean something similar, but they are not identical. In this passage 'look for' means something more like 'expect' or 'hope for'. (In fact 'look for' always means something rather different to plain 'look'). 'Glance', as usual, means 'to take a quick look'; while 'behold' is an old-fashioned word meaning 'to see': perhaps the writer has used it here because it fitted better with the 'ancient vengeful deity' than merely saying 'I saw'.

The point of this is that synonyms are rarely *identical* in meaning. Two words are often very *similar* in meaning, but they *suggest* different things. A *glance* is not the same as a *look,* and a *look* is not the same as a *stare*. It is important to get the right idea behind the words you use. Returning to the passage again: though 'I stared up at his angry face' is not all that different from 'I glanced up at his angry face', it *is* different enough for us to form two separate pictures of the scene. We visualise the glance as a quick, frightened darting of the eyes before looking away again; but we think of the stare as as a fixed gaze, perhaps with eyes slowly widening in fear. — Well, perhaps we do not quite see all that in one word, but you can understand the point. . . .

There are two other sets of synonyms in that passage:—

sympathy, compassion and *pity*   *ruthless, implacable* and *vengeful.*

So how would it sound if we took out ALL the synonyms:—

> I looked up at his ruthless face looking for some pity, but his eyes were like steel in that ruthless face. The face I looked at was that of an ancient, ruthless deity, devoid of all pity. I could expect no pity from such as he.

A bit tedious, don't you think? Remember, above all, NEVER BORE YOUR READER!

2

(a) Try to give TEN synonyms for EACH of these definitions.
The words themselves will not all be exact synonyms of each other, but they must fit the definitions.

(1)   Something you sit on
(2)   Something you write or draw with
(3)   To look at
(4)   To promise
(5)   Happy
(6)   Beautiful

(30 — ½ each word)

(b) For each of the following words give two synonyms that stick as closely as possible to the meaning of the original word. For example: *face — visage, countenance; angry — annoyed, irritated.*

(1)   help (verb)   (5)   conquer   (8)   perfume (noun)
(2)   little   (6)   thin   (9)   ban (verb)
(3)   quiet   (7)   choose   (10) copy (verb)
(4)   huge

(20 — 1 per word)

(c) For each of these words give one *exact* synonym, that could be substituted for the word virtually any time it was used, whatever its meaning:—

(1)   globe   (11) expensive
(2)   cows   (12) merriment
(3)   axe   (13) soil (noun)
(4)   finger   (14) soil (verb)
(5)   allow   (15) revenge
(6)   weep   (16) try (verb)
(7)   sufficient   (17) exact (adj.)
(8)   eraser   (18) quarter (noun)
(9)   machine   (19) island
(10) lantern   (20) angle

(20)

(d) In the following sentence *angry* and its corresponding adverb (*angrily*) and noun (*anger*) are overused. Rewrite the sentence substituting a different synonym in each case. Notice that one synonym, *irritations*, has already been employed, so you should avoid that as well. In the process try to improve the sentence. It should not be difficult.

He had started the day in an *angry* mood, and as his morning came to be marked by a series of minor irritations, he became more *angry*, until by lunch time his every word was an *angry* snarl, objects were banged down *angrily* on the desk, and his answers to quite innocuous letters bristled with scarcely suppressed *anger*.

(10 — 2 per synonym)

(e) Part of using synonyms is learning the meanings of words. So stop pretending you know what *innocuous* means; look it up; and then write for it: (1) five synonyms, and (2) five antonyms. An antonym is the opposite of a synonym, — and means 'opposite'. After all, if you know what a word means, you should also be able to say precisely what it does not mean . . .

(10)

3

FACTSHEET TWO

SYNONYMS (2) — ACCURACY

Look back at the passage with which we started Factsheet One. We have not quite worked it to death yet. You will remember that we made the point that words like 'glance' and 'stare' are both synonyms for 'look'. In fact they are also better words to use than 'look'. Though they are its synonyms they each stand for a different sort of 'look'. If the passage had said "I looked up at his face", we would not not have known whether it was the long stare of terror, or the quick apprehensive glance.

When you have a selection of synonyms to choose from (as you often do), try to pick the most precise. The clearer your *word picture* is, the better your reader will see what you mean. The idea of a *word picture* is a good way of thinking of it. A little child when painting will do the faces bright pink or dark brown; a more experienced artist will know that more precise, more varied, and subtler shades are needed. Also, if you take the trouble to think about what words you use, you will be forced to think more carefully and more clearly about exactly what idea or impression you actually *want* to convey.

Look at these examples:—
(a) I have *looked at* your *writing*, Miss Simms, and I found it very *full* but rather *boring*.
(b) I have *studied* your *essay*, Miss Simms, and I found it very *detailed*, but rather *repetitive*.

Both say much the same thing, but (b) is more precise; it contains more information. From (a) we did not know how closely the writing had been looked at ('studied' in fact), that the writing was an 'essay', in what way it was 'full' or why it was also 'boring'. If you were a teacher, and poor Miss Simms was your student, she would probably rather hear (b) from you than (a).

Have a look at these three sentences as well:—
(a) The *officer* ordered his *soldiers* to *attack* the enemy *position*.
(b) The *lieutenant* ordered his *platoon* to *charge* the enemy *dug-out*.
(c) The *general* ordered his *division* to *beseige* the enemy *fortress*.

The trouble with (a) is that it is so vague it could apply equally well to (b) or (c). They both tell us how important the officer was; just how many men were involved (a platoon might be ten, a division might be ten thousand); what sort of attack was planned, and what sort of position the enemy had (and there is a good deal of difference between a 'dug-out' and a 'fortress'). So (b) and (c) describe two totally different operations, — yet from (a) we could never guess which was meant.

Choose your words carefully, and use synonyms to improve your accuracy and precision. The simplest thing to consider when doing so, is to ask yourself the question 'How serious?' or 'How important?' With many collections of synonyms you can make up what we might call a 'table of intensity':—

Annoyance, irritation, fury and *rage* are all synonyms for *anger,* but obviously 'fury' and 'rage' are more extreme forms of anger than 'annoyance' or 'irritation'.

Likewise *flicker* and *inferno* may both be synonyms for *flame* or *fire,* but which one you use is going to make a great deal of difference to your meaning. 'The house was consumed in a raging *inferno*' is better than 'The house was consumed in a raging *fire*'; 'He blew on the embers until he obtained a faint *flicker*' is similarly better than 'He blew on the embers until he obtained a faint *flame*'.

Above all, avoid words that have almost no meaning, like *nice* and *pleasant.* 'Nice' once meant 'precise' or 'exact', now it is just a vague expression of approval. Think what you really want to say, and then decide which word says it most clearly and most precisely.

(a) The following sentences are rather vague. Try to make them more precise by substituting synonyms for the words in italics. (Where a word is very vague, you will find that you have a very wide choice of acceptable alternatives.)

    (1)   We heard the sound of a *big bang* from the bank.
    (2)   Bill's writing is *poor* and his essays very *bad*.
    (3)   I have never seen such a *large vegetable*.
    (4)   The *boss* explained the *drawing* to the *employee*.
    (5)   Have you *done* the *work* for the accounts yet?
    (6)   The weight of the *stuff* was too great for the *vehicle* and the *man* refused to take it.
    (7)   Sheila found the *book* very *hard*.
    (8)   The *leader told* the *people* to prepare for *difficulties*.

                                                (20)

(b) In the following passage replace the words in italics with synonyms once again. Try to use words that are more precise, and, if possible, also more vivid.

    She wore an old dress, which had once had a *pretty* pattern but now was faded and *dirty*. Her hair was *dirty* and *lay* across a haunted and unhappy face. Her eyes *looked* from side to side as if she was *worried* that something *unpleasant* was about to happen. Her *hands* were *closed* tightly, ready to fight if she did not first run away.

                                                (10)

(c) In each of these sentences there is a pair of synonyms. Write out the words concerned in each case. Remember, synonyms are often *similar* in meaning rather than *identical*.

    (1)   Her vague apprehension grew slowly into genuine fear.
    (2)   The colours of the tapestry were dimmed by dust and time, until they had become the hues of a faded rainbow in a wan and watery sky.
    (3)   I have never put my trust in the promises of politicians, for I find they ever repay faith with deceit.
    (4)   The sight I saw before me was a vision of another world beyond our knowledge or our strangest dreams.
    (5)   The flicker of defiance in his eye became a dulled ember, as he shrugged his final submission to the inevitable.

                                        (10 — 1 each word)

(d) The following passage is not very nice . . . See if you can improve it by substituting synonyms that actually mean something for the words in italics.

    It was a *nice* day, so Elvira decided that she would go for a *nice* walk. She packed a *nice* selection of food — a *nice* apple, some *nice* meat sandwiches, and a *nice* piece of pie. "That should make a *nice* picnic," she thought, as she changed into a *nice* summer dress and put on that *nice* hat her mother had given her for her birthday. As she opened the front door, the first *nasty* drops of rain began to fall.

                                                (10)

(e) Here are five groups of synonyms. Arrange each group in order of 'intensity', starting with the least and ending with the greatest:—

    (1)   fire   conflagration   inferno   flicker
    (2)   torment   twinge   ache   agony
    (3)   prehistoric   ancient   antique   old
    (4)   read   peruse   skim   study
    (5)   raised   exalted   lofty   high

                                                (10)

FACTSHEET THREE

SYNONYMS (3) — SLANT

We have already talked a little about using words to create the right impression — the image *behind* the words. Two very similar words, which if you tried to write their meanings down might even appear identical, may have very different *shades* of meaning. Look at these two sentences:—

(a) Bright, uninterrupted sunshine bathes an extensive sweep of golden sands.

(b) Glaring, unending sunlight beats down on a vast tract of ochre sand.

The first one might well be from a holiday brochure describing a tropical beach. The second sounds like the middle of the desert with the vultures already hovering. Neither beach nor desert is mentioned. The words used give those particular impressions. It is all done by way of the particular synonyms, or near-synonyms, chosen. 'Bright' and 'glaring' are just two ways of saying the same thing. 'Ochre' and 'golden' both essentially mean 'yellow', while 'extensive' and 'vast' are just different ways of saying 'very big'. If you were to cut the sentences in half, and then transpose the parts, you would get a rather curious result:—

(c) Glaring, unending sunlight bathes an extensive sweep of golden sands.

As you can see, the impression is confused (unless you are trying to suggest that the beach is good, but rather spoilt by excessive sunshine!)

This use of carefully chosen words to convey the desired impression, known as the *slant* of a piece of writing, can be a dangerous thing too. Newspapers, radio and television do it all the time — and not just in advertisements. It is an attempt to influence the way we think about things, and since we are not usually alert to the particular words being used, it often works. There is a saying:— "One man's terrorist is another man's freedom fighter". Which of the two 'slanted' words is used will have an effect on how we form our opinions.

Look at these two sentences:—

(d) His angry dad gave the teen-aged boy a hard smacking.

(e) His enraged father gave the young child a severe beating.

The second sentence is describing precisely the same thing as the first. The words used are synonyms for those in the first sentence, and no words with different meanings have been introduced (for example, 'cruel' has not replaced 'hard'). 'Angry' might well mean 'enraged'; many consider 'teen-aged' as 'young'; and a 'boy' is indeed a 'child'. It is not the meaning of the words that has changed, it is the impression which is deliberately being given.

Look at these pairs of expressions, with opposite slants:—

unprovoked aggression — surprise attack   major economies — swingeing cuts

intrepid hero — rash adventurer   eliminate our opposition — kill our enemies

Learn to use the technique when you want to persuade someone; but do not let it be used on you!

Finally, you may know that there is a kind of dictionary of synonyms, called a *thesaurus*. If you have not seen one, ask your librarian for it. It is quite difficult to use, and you need a dictionary to check meanings as well, but it is a good way to broaden your vocabulary, as long as you don't go over the top, and write:—

"I lay under the necessity of anticipating the omnibus for epochs" when you mean "I had to wait ages for the bus".

Remember, in using synonyms you are aiming for three things — VARIETY, ACCURACY, and THE RIGHT IMPRESSION.

(a) Here is a page from a hotel brochure produced by someone with a faulty phrase book. See if you can correct the impression he has given by changing the words in italics to others with a rather different slant. . .

Our beaches here are immensely *overcrowded.* You cannot fail to be delighted by the *precipitous* trackways that wind down to *cramped* and *inaccessible* coves. You will thrill to the *immense tidal-waves* that *smash* over the *boulders* of the beach. Temperatures are always *extreme,* and we can promise you a *penetrating sunburn.* But don't worry, you can also rely on the regular *hurricanes* to cool you down. In the town, the *uproar* of *riotous* laughter fills the streets by night, while by day you can listen to the *weird* stories of the *decrepit savages* as they sit outside the taverna. In the markets you will find a flourishing *barter* in antiques *stolen* by enterprising local *grave-robbers.*

(20)

(b) This time what seems to have happened is that a pupil in school has obtained a thesaurus, — and has been using it somewhat unwisely. In each sentence *one* word needs replacing with a more suitable synonym.

(1)   The Scouts eagerly warmed their hands on the conflagration.

(2)   We haven't seen your physiognomy around here lately, Joe.

(3)   I'm afraid I do rather abominate rice pudding.

(4)   That awful Mrs Woodhall was there, and you know how multiloquous she can be.

(5)   "I find the children in my class very insurgent", said Mr Sparkes.

(6)   As she was cutting the roses Louise felt a sudden mortification on her finger.

(7)   "I wish you would wash your hair, Simon. It's very putrid", said his mother.

(8)   I am anticipating the three o'clock to Hatch End.

(9)   Ah, I see it converging now.

(10)   As usual, it is rather dilatory today.

(20)

(c) Rewrite each of the following sentences, changing the words in italics so that you give the sentence a particular *slant,* either in favour of, or opposed to what is being described. For example, if you wanted to slant "The fête will be opened by an important person" favourably, you could replace 'important person' with 'distinguished visitor' or 'popular celebrity'. Remember, it is the sentence as a whole you are trying to slant.

(1)   We must now consider the recent *reduction* in *expenditure.* (UNFAVOURABLE.)

(2)   Are we prepared to fund this *unusual scheme?* (TWO — (a) FAVOURABLE; (b) UNFAVOURABLE).

(3)   Mr Wood is a *well-known businessman.* (UNFAVOURABLE).

(4)   The house is *small* and on a *busy* street. (TWO — (a) FAVOURABLE; (b) UNFAVOURABLE).

(5)   In an *impassioned* speech he demanded immediate *unilateral* disarmament. (UNFAVOURABLE).

(6)   We have today launched *revenge raids* against enemy cities. (FAVOURABLE).

(7)   We believe that *youthful offenders* should face tough sentences. (FAVOURABLE).

(8)   Mr Disraeli was a *well-known politician.* (FAVOURABLE).

(20 — 2 per word)

FACTSHEET FOUR

SIMILES (1)

A SIMILE is a COMPARISON. There are two common ways of making comparisons in speech and writing. The first of these is done by using the link word *like*, or some similar word. Look at these examples:—

Mrs Batson has been *like a mother* to that poor boy.

The Assyrian came down *like a wolf on the fold*.

He reacted to the news *like a mad bull*.

Her eyes were *like stars reflected in dark pools* . . .

What we are doing when we make this sort of comparison is trying to bring the scene or situation we are describing alive, by referring our description to something graphic and vivid which the reader will immediately recognise and be able to picture.

We are also using a kind of shorthand, cutting out a long and possibly complicated description of what we mean by summing it all up in a simile. If we were to expand the first of the above examples to explain exactly what we meant, we would need something of this sort:—

"Mrs Batson has always been very kind to that boy. She has taken him into her own house, fed him, provided him with clothes, even looked after him when he was ill . . ." etc. If you want to do a full description like this (perhaps to emphasize your point), you can do so. The simile lacks detail, but it gets there quicker. You can also do both:— start with your simile to create the impression you want, then develop it with a fuller description.

The phrases *as if* and *as though* can also be used in the same way as *like*, but they are not so direct. They can often suggest that, though we are making a comparison, we do not quite believe it is a true or accurate one, as in:—

She treated him as if he were her own son.

He reacted to the news as if he were a mad bull.

Notice the odd form of the verb — 'were' when you would expect 'was'. This form is called the 'subjunctive', and is used precisely when what you are saying is doubtful or just a possibility.

The two examples we have just seen both give the impression that the words 'although of course he was not' could be added to the end.

Some comparisons using *like* have been around for a long time, and though they were striking when first used they have lost a great deal of their force, in fact they have become CLICHÉS.

A cliché (notice the accent on the final E; the word is pronounced 'clee-shay') is an idea or expression that has been used too often, become too familiar, or ceased to have much meaning. *Like a bull in a china shop*, or *like a bull at a gate* have both been overworked, and because it is rather similar we would probably therefore want to think of something rather more original than *like a mad bull* as used in one of the examples above. As with synonyms we are trying to improve the quality of our description, so the aim should be for newness or originality, and effectiveness or realism.

Look at some more examples:—

The stern of the sinking ship stood up *like a gravestone* out of the waves.

The ship screamed her torment, *like a dying creature*, as she struck the reef.

Alderman Sprocket arose *like a sea-lion roused to the defence of its harem*.

She fastened on Mr Dimple *like a well-trained retriever on a particularly plump bird*.

His face was large, pink and lumpy, *like a badly made blancmange*.

(a) In the following sentences insert a *single word* simile of your own to complete the comparison. (You can insert or remove *a, an, the* as you please).

   (1)   Our little boat floated like a . . . . . . on the waves.
   (2)   The water felt like . . . . . . on my fevered brow.
   (3)   He began to climb the cliff like a . . . . . .
   (4)   In his rage he behaved like a . . . . . .
   (5)   The heavens opened, and the rain fell like a . . . . . .
   (6)   I will not say that that baby is ugly; merely that it looks like a . . . . . .
   (7)   Amidst all the chaos and upheaval, she alone stood like a . . . . . . in the surges.
   (8)   After the shouting and screams the sudden silence was like the . . . . . .
   (9)   Though he wriggled like an . . . . . . , at last I caught hold of him.
  (10)   The sea burnt like a . . . . . . in the sunset.

                                                                               (10)

(b) The following similes are all in common use (and many or all of them may have become clichés), — but what do they mean?

   (i)   EXPLAIN in your own words what each phrase means.   (15 — 1½ each)
   (ii)   USE each phrase in a sentence so that its meaning is clear.   (15 — 1½ each)

(1) Like a bull in a china shop	(6)	Like water off a duck's back
(2) Like a cat on hot bricks	(7)	As though her heart would break
(3) Like a drowned rat	(8)	A memory like a sieve
(4) Like a rat in a trap	(9)	To hang on like grim death
(5) Like a duck out of water	(10)	To turn up like a bad penny

(c) Look back at the section at the end of the Factsheet. For each of the five examples given, explain the meaning of the simile used and say why it is an effective (or an ineffective) comparison.

                                                                     (10 — 2 each)

(d) In each of these sentences a rather ordinary and overworked simile is used. Rewrite the sentences, using a new simile of your own. You can use more than one word, but try not to use more than five or six, as it is easy to lose track of complicated similes.

   (1)   Her tiny hands felt *like ice*.
   (2)   You will have to run *like the wind* if you are ever going to catch him.
   (3)   She has worked *like a Trojan* to get that job finished.
   (4)   Outside the bedroom stood my little brother, grinning *like a Cheshire cat*.
   (5)   Of course I don't like to spread gossip but they do say her husband drinks *like a fish*.
   (6)   You moved *like greased lightning* when you sat on that toasting fork.
   (7)   You had better be careful; the boss is *like a bear with a sore head* today.
   (8)   She looked *as though butter wouldn't melt in her mouth*.
   (9)   The two boys entered the headmaster's study *like lambs to the slaughter*.
  (10)   He had warned them that the next time they broke a window he would come down on them *like a ton of bricks*.

                                                                            (20)

NOTE:— In numbers 4, 5 and 10 you may want to use a different verb which fits your new simile better. You can do this in these sentences (and others if it is really necessary) as long as you keep the same overall meaning.

SIMILES (2)

A different kind of comparison is the type which uses *as* .... *as* ....
You find this in expressions like:—

I'll never play tennis *as* well *as* you, even if I practice for years.

I want another piece exactly *as* long *as* this one.

It isn't *as* easy *as* you thought, is it, my girl?

These are what we might call practical comparisons, used about a specific thing or action. You need to be careful that you say what you mean though:—

"She hates him as much as I" does NOT mean the same as "She hates him as much as me".

The first one means:— "She hates him as much as I hate him".

The second one means:— "She hates him as much as she hates me".

More important from our point of view in learning how to improve our essay or composition writing is what we might call the *descriptive* comparison. Many of these are traditional, almost proverbial, and you do hear them quite often:—

as heavy as lead	as old as the hills	as deaf as a post	as cunning as a fox
as blind as a bat	as white as snow	as green as grass	as daft as a brush

as thick as two short planks (a more modern invention, but already over-used).

You need to be aware of these, and to know what they mean, but you should be careful when you use them in your own writing. Your aims, particularly in a piece of description, are to be *original, imaginative,* and *expressive.* Phrases which have been used innumerable times before do not really qualify under these headings. Use them in dialogue — the actual words people say in direct speech — by all means. They can help to make speech more realistic.

Otherwise, make it a rule:— "Avoid clichés like the plague". (This is a good way to remember it because, as you will have instantly noticed it contains a simile, *avoid like the plague,* which is itself a cliché. You did notice, didn't you . . .?) Instead, make up new similes of your own, that have not been used before, that are striking, and that get across the exact idea you want.

"As old as Methuselah" (he is an Old Testament character who lived for a long time) does not mean much any more; "as old as the hills" is better, because it is a more vivid image, but it has been used very many times; "as old as sin" is more expressive still, and gives a particular idea, but it is not original. But I do not think I have seen "as old as death" or "as old as hope" which could both be used in (very different) descriptive writing.

"As smooth as velvet" is of course a cliché, — and a more original expression, such as "as smooth as a snake" or "as smooth as cream" might suit the impression you want to give rather better.

"As soft as butter" may be the usual simile, but you might well prefer "as soft as a slug" because it fits better into the picture you are creating.

You can have sarcastic similes, like "as clear as mud". You can revive old similes with a touch of humour:— "Our Jim's as sharp as a tack, — and just as flat on the head." And you can have pungent or biting similes like "as cold as charity". (Try to work out exactly what this means; what is the connection between coldness and charity? — Also, if you don't know what pungent means, hadn't you better look it up?)

So, get to know the commonplace similes, but be careful how you use them. At the same time, and more importantly, try to develop your own, original similes.

(a)　Complete the following common or proverbial similes with the usual word or words:—

1.　As brown as...............................
2.　As clean as ....
3.　As like as ....
4.　As keen as................................
5.　As regular as............................

6.　As silent as..................................
7.　As cool as....................................
8.　As large as...................................
9.　As tough as..................................
10. As gentle as..................................

(10)

(b)　In exactly the same way, for each of the following similes there are two alternative forms in common use. So for each simile, give the two possible completions:—

1.　As old as....................................
2.　As fresh as ....
3.　As easy as ....

4.　As warm as...................................
5.　As sharp as...................................

(10)

(c)　In the following it is not the comparison which is missing, but the thing that is being compared. Complete them with the usual word.

1.　As.....................as a monkey
2.　As.....................as pie
3.　As.....................as a doornail
4.　As.....................as a rake
5.　As.....................as a mule

6.　As ....as a trivet
7.　As ....as Croesus
8.　As ....as Punch
9.　As ....as a sandboy
10. As ....as ninepence

(10)

(d)　This time your job is to make up your own similes for the following. Try to be original. (If there is a common simile already doing the job, it is not what we want here). Also try to make the word *fit* with the comparison. ("As strong as a banana" is not a good simile, — unless you are being sarcastic). Try to use only one or two words for each answer. Do NOT use the names of people you know . . .

1.　As pale as..................................
2.　As strange as ....
3.　As sore as ....
4.　As crooked as............................
5.　As sad as...................................

6.　As patient as ....
7.　As dismal as..................................
8.　As lazy as.....................................
9.　As boring as..................................
10. As fearful as..................................

(10)

(e)　Here is a collection of commonplace similes, — clichés in fact. In each case replace the word or words of the comparison (which are in italics) with a new and original simile of your own. (Try not to make it too long or complicated.)

1.　As light as *a feather*
2.　As strong as *an ox*
3.　As deep as *the ocean*
4.　As high as *the sky*
5.　As busy as *a bee*

6.　As easy as *falling off a log*
7.　As plain as *the nose on your face*
8.　As clever as *a cartload of monkeys*
9.　As poor as a *church mouse*
10. As innocent as *a new-born babe*

(10)

(f)　In each of these sentences, insert a simile of your own that fits the general impression. This time they can be longer if you wish.

1.　The long sweep of the desolate moor was as lonely as...

2.　I looked in horror at the bloody knife in my hand, then at the body which lay there as still as .... at my feet.

3.　The lantern shone out, far off still, but as welcome as ....

4.　The sigh of the breezes, as soothing as.. lulled us into sleep.

5.　In her eyes I saw only a swirling hatred, and her words when they came were bitter as............................

(10)

FACTSHEET SIX

Back on Worksheet Four you had to fill in the simile in this sentence:—

"The sea burnt like ....in the sunset."

No doubt you filled in some suitable word (it is not after all very difficult!) but you probably did not notice that this sentence contains another, less apparent comparison:—

"The sea burnt....."

Well, no it did not. In fact it was *as if* the sea burnt. But from the way the sentence is phrased, you would think that it really happened. In the sentence:— "As the oil spilt out from the stricken tanker, the surface of the sea caught alight and burnt fiercely" we have a *literal* use of the words. In other words they mean what they say, no more, no less. In the example we started with, though, the words have what is known as a *metaphorical* or *figurative* use.

(There is a foolish tendency to use 'literally' when 'metaphorically' is meant, as in:— "I was literally bowled over by his words" — which is literally impossible!)

The sort of comparison where the thing apparently *becomes* what it is compared with is called a metaphor.

We use metaphors constantly and most of the time without even noticing it:—

These constant interruptions have disturbed my *flow*.

I have no intention of *crawling* to that self-important little man.

This entire plan *hinges* on complete and utter secrecy.

This nation will never *break* faith with her allies.

If we take the words in italics literally, then *flow* belongs properly to rivers, while *crawling* definitely suggests movement on the hands and knees; the only things *hinging* on hinges are doors; and *breaking* is definitely both physical and fairly violent. But we all understand immediately what is meant by 'the flow of speech'. 'To hinge on' meaning 'to depend on' is so widely used that its metaphorical nature and all connection with doors is virtually unnoticed. 'Break' is now used in many senses that do not have the original idea of 'smash into pieces'; for that matter we can *break into* song, or *crack* a joke before we *break down* in tears.

The use of very many words in this way makes our language more rich and lively (and, as it happens, in that sentence *rich* and *lively* were both used metaphorically!) But it is not these that we want to look at so much as the use of new and interesting metaphors which can make our own writing even richer and more lively.

Among the examples of similes at the bottom of Factsheet Four was this sentence:—

"The ship screamed her torment, like a dying creature, as she struck the reef."

Here the simile is a piece of additional description of a metaphor:— "The ship screamed her torment." This is a particular sort of metaphor called personification, where an object is treated as if it were a living creature that could experience and feel emotions. What is being done is to take the sound (a high pitched screech probably, no doubt sounding like a very loud scream) and build from it an unusual description that will catch the attention. The difference between a simile and a metaphor is that the simile makes it clear that a comparison is being made; words are used, like *like* or *as . . . . as*, to state the fact of a comparison. A metaphor on the other hand transforms the object into what it is being compared with. A metaphor can very often be much stronger and more direct than a simile.

(a) In each of the following pairs of sentences, one of them uses words *literally*, and the other uses them *metaphorically*. Copy out the sentences and next to each write the words 'literal' or 'metaphorical' depending on which is which. Pay particular attention to the words in italics in each sentence, as they are the ones that matter most in making your decision.

(1) (i)   Amidst the driving rain I could *kindle* no *flame* from my wet tinder.
    (ii)   Her words *kindled* a *flame* of hope in his heart.
(2) (i)   *Angry* clouds had been *threatening* rain all day.
    (ii)   The *angry* father *threatened* his naughty son.
(3) (i)   I have made my judgement *in the light of* experience.
    (ii)   *In the light* of the sun we can see our shadows.
(4) (i)   I was *afraid* you would prick yourself with the *point* of that needle.
    (ii)   I'm *afraid* I miss the *point* of your speech.
(5) (i)   No sooner was Mr Oakwood dead, than the *vultures* of the family descended in the hope of rich *pickings*.
    (ii)   A solitary *vulture picked* at the shreds of flesh on poor Carstairs' bare, white bones.

                                                                                              (20)

(b) In the following sentences, do exactly the same. This time, however, you are not given the key words. You have to find them for yourself. As well as saying which are metaphorical and which literal, underline the words that have led you to your choice.

(1) (i)   The atmosphere was electric as the Prime Minister rose to speak.
    (ii)   The lightning of an electric storm flashed among the scudding clouds of the upper atmosphere.
(2) (i)   This practice has mushroomed in recent years.
    (ii)   Alice hid under the giant mushroom.
(3) (i)   All through the day the pack had stalked them, and by night the eyes of the wolves shone beyond the dim circle of light from their camp-fire.
    (ii)   Far amidst the haunted wastes wolf-eyed madness stalked their path.
(4) (i)   Even the craftiest criminal must one day face arrest by Sergeant Death.
    (ii)   The appropriately-named Sergeant Death, with eleven constables from Wollagong, planned to arrest the entire Wilson Gang in an ambush at Tombstone Crossing.
(5) (i)   I have set my hand to the plough of educational reform.
    (ii)   He paused, wiped his brow, and rested his gnarled old hand on the plough, gazing out at the wide sweep of the fields before him.

                                                                                              (20)

(c) In each of the following sentences there is a metaphorical word or expression. Underline them all, and say what each of them *means*.

(1)   I have no axe to grind in the matter of fixing the rent for these houses.
(2)   The candidate for the position of Treasurer was bombarded with questions about his recent conviction for fraud.
(3)   A good friend is not only our helper in times of trouble, but also a mirror of our conscience.
(4)   Dr. Johnstone of Islington has for some time been seen as the rising star of the party in that borough.
(5)   While I have been slaving over a hot stove you've been out having a good time with your so-called friends.

                                                                                              (20)

FACTSHEET SEVEN

METAPHORS (2)

With metaphors as with similes we want to avoid expressions which were once vivid comparisons with plenty of life in them, but have now become clichés (over-used expressions). "She has a heart of stone" was once a very striking comparison (as no doubt were the equivalent similes "She has a heart like stone" or "Her heart is as hard as stone"). But after the first few thousand times of use, it became something of a *twice told tale*, and of course a bit *old hat*. (The words in italics are two more metaphors that have declined into clichés).

There are many others:— "He had to *eat his words*" . . . . "We must *explore every avenue*" . . . . *Icy fingers ran up my spine*" (unless they did so literally) . . . .
See if you can think of any more; there are quite a few around.

Where a phrase is still obviously a metaphor, but is so over-worked that it has become a cliché, it is better to do without altogether, and just use a straightforward description. If you want to use a metaphor, it needs to be original, to fit the particular piece of description you are writing, and to catch the attention of the reader. After all, the purpose of the metaphor is to make what you are writing more lively and descriptive, — and in particular *more interesting*.

Of course you can sometimes revive old metaphors with a new twist. ("A new twist":— surely that has not become a cliché yet!)
"As I entered the examination room my blood turned to water; it would have been more use if it had turned to ink."
"Her heart was hard, but so were her arteries, and I didn't give her long to live."

The trouble with humour, particularly if you are writing an essay or composition in an examination, is that examiners are not noted for their appreciation of it. Only try to be funny in a piece of writing if you are sure it works, and the piece of writing needs it.

There is another metaphorical swamp into which it is easy to stray if you are not careful:— the MIXED METAPHOR. Because we use metaphors so much, and often without even noticing we are doing so, it is easy to put two very different ones next to each other, or to start with one metaphor and then move on to another. The result can be to produce an image in the reader's mind which, though very funny, is not quite what you intended:—
"Now we have our backs to the wall, we must put our shoulder to the wheel and pull our socks up." (Thank goodness we don't have to put our nose to the grindstone as well!)
"He launched the project off his own bat". (So much cheaper than off a slipway).

Here is a more famous mixed metaphor, supposed to have been said in the House of Commons:—
"Mr Speaker, I smell a rat. I see it floating in the air; and if it is not nipped in the bud, it will burst forth into a terrible conflagration that will deluge the world".
It is worth going through that sentence, sorting out each metaphor used, and comparing it with the one before.

So you need to think carefully what you are saying when you use metaphors. But if used properly, they can improve your writing very greatly. Look at these examples:—
"The notes clambered up the steps of the crescendo, paused, and then held their ears. . . ."
"Ghosts of distant tea-parties returned to haunt her with their rattling bone china. . . ."
"Wolf-toothed hunger gnawed at his vitals. . . ."
"A pale flower of fear blossomed in her heart. . . ."
"The gloomy silence stalked their steps. . . ."
"To cast your pearls before swine is pointless; to cast them before oysters is also tasteless. . . ."
Can you work out the full meaning behind some of these?

(a) Write out the following sentences and underline the metaphors in each of them.

   (1) We must leave no stone unturned in our search for a new candidate.

   (2) I think I begin to see the drift of your argument.

   (3) Your behaviour today has been the last straw, so you can go to bed right now.

   (4) Mrs Thompson is in the evening of her years; soon her life's journey will be over. (2)

   (5) He may be a rough diamond, but he's got a heart of gold. (2)

   (6) If you think she'll lift a finger to help you, you're living in a fool's paradise. (2)

   (7) There's no need to get on your high horse just because I make a simple suggestion.

                                                                                 (10)

(b) None of the metaphors in (a) were original, and some or all of them may well have become clichés. Rewrite each sentence, using a straightforward, literal description in place of each of the ten metaphors you have underlined.

                                           (20 — 2 per metaphor replaced)

(c) In each of the following sentences there is a confused or mixed metaphor. Explain briefly in each case what the problem is by identifying the two (or more) metaphors that have become linked, and saying why they do not go together very well.

   (1) I had decided to burn my boats and embark on the venture.

   (2) They have held out an olive branch, but I do not see anything concrete coming out of it.

   (3) They are hiding their heads in the sand and looking round for a scapegoat.

   (4) The Chief Constable is nothing but a whited sepulchre tied up with red tape.

   (5) His statement was a bolt from the blue which deluged us with bones of contention. (3)

   (6) He is a wolf in sheep's clothing who wants to set the Thames on fire by burning the candle at both ends. (3)

   (7) He may be a broken reed, but I shall have my pound of flesh from him.

   (8) I think his humble pie was just crocodile tears.

   (9) Beware of Lord Lune; there's a touch of the cloven hoof in his blue blood.

  (10) He has made a clean breast of the skeleton in his closet.

                                                            (20 — 2 each)

(d) Invent metaphors of your own that answer the following general definitions. Your metaphors may be single words, or several words, — but the main thing is that they should be NEW.

   (1) A large, heavy, slow-moving person

   (2) A new plan, untried before

   (3) A sudden hope, where previously there was none

   (4) A smooth, calm sea in the moonlight

   (5) A long and difficult task

   (6) Waiting for something to happen

   (7) A large number of unexpected events following one after another

   (8) An important person who is well aware of his or her own importance

   (9) Fear

  (10) Life

                                                                         (10)

(e) Now use each of the metaphors you have invented in the above exercise in a sentence of your own to demonstrate that it does work as a piece of description.

                                                                         (10)

FACTSHEET EIGHT

DESCRIPTION (1)

A great deal of what we have covered so far has been about description. In looking at synonyms we were concerned with getting the right word, and the most striking word, for exactly what we wanted to say. Then in talking about similes and metaphors we were looking at ways of making descriptions more lively and interesting by the use of comparisons. But when we come down to it, description in stories or compositions will depend very largely on the two categories of descriptive words, adjectives and adverbs. As you know (of course) an adjective describes (correct word: *qualifies*) a noun, and an adverb describes (correct word: *modifies*) a verb.

When young children write, they tend to concentrate on the events, and any adjectives that sneak in follow the verb *to be* in little sentences of their own; the only adverb you are likely to get is *suddenly*. Look at this example to see what I mean:—

"I was going up the road. There was castle at the top of the hill. I could see it. I went up to the door. I pushed it and it opened. Suddenly there was a sound. I was scared."

This sort of writing is not bad or wrong, — it is more like the rough sketch, before you start to paint the real picture. So let's take another example, the sort of thing that you as a trainee writer could have written, and see what we can do with it.

"The children climbed the path up the side of the cliff. They kept looking behind them, but Mr Jakes did not appear. The tide was washing into the cave mouth where he lay. They began to wonder if Tim could have killed him with the mallet."

Once again there is nothing *wrong* with this, but it is almost totally lacking in adjectives and adverbs. If we want to bring the scene alive to the reader, we need to let him know more about what is going on. In the middle of a book, where the reader already has a great deal of background information, you might not want to slow the action down with too much description, but you are (probably) not writing books yet. So, how can we develop this short paragraph in an essay or composition? — A good way to start is to ask some questions about what we *are* told:—

How many children?

How did they climb the path? Were they in a hurry?

What sort of path was it?

Why were they looking behind them? And so on . . .

We answer the questions with adjectives and adverbs:—

"The *three* children *breathlessly* climbed the *winding, narrow* path up the *steep* side of the cliff. They looked *anxiously* behind them, but Mr Jakes did not appear. The tide was *already* washing *steadily* into the cave mouth where he lay, *perhaps still unconscious*. They began to wonder *uneasily* if Tim could *really* have killed him with the mallet."

The thirteen adjectives and adverbs we have added may possibly be too many, and clutter the story up — but the action still seems to move quite quickly. On the other hand, the additions certainly do give us a clearer picture of what is happening. We know more about what the children are feeling and thinking because of the adverbs *breathlessly, anxiously, uneasily* — and we also know that there are *three* children. We have a more accurate idea of the cliff path, and we know much more about the state of Mr Jakes:— *unconscious*, and *possibly still unconscious* — which does give the mention of the incoming tide rather more significance. It is like painting in the detail on to the sketch (to continue with the *metaphor* we used above); the sketch is good — as a sketch, but the completed painting is better.

It is very good training to force yourself for a few pieces of written work to give every noun an adjective (two adjectives for those wishing to be romantic novelists when they grow up) and every verb an adverb. When you are writing, *think* about description — not just striking similes and clever metaphors, but simple adjectives and adverbs.

(a) In each of the following passages insert adverbs or adjectives in place of the words in brackets. Try to make the words you use all work together to give the same impression, so that the passage as a whole gives a particular impression or idea to the reader. (You will notice that the first piece is the first example used in the Factsheet).

(1) I was going (ADVERB) up the (ADJECTIVE) road. There was a (2 ADJECTIVES) castle at the top of the (ADJECTIVE) hill. I could (ADVERB) see it. I went (ADVERB) up to the (ADJECTIVE) door, I pushed it, and it (ADVERB) opened. Suddenly there was a (ADJECTIVE) sound. I was scared.

(2) The (ADJ) trees shook (ADV) in the (ADJ) wind. The (ADJ) sky was (ADV) full of (ADJ) clouds racing (ADV) by. She shivered (ADV) and pulled the collar of her (ADJ) coat (ADV) up round her neck.

(3) In the (ADJ) rain the (ADJ) light of the (ADJ) street lamps danced (ADV) across the (ADJ) road. Cars shrieked (ADV) by, scattering the (ADJ) light in droplets of (ADJ) colour that swirled (ADV) into the air, then fell like (ADJ) embers back to the road.

(4) (ADJ) children played (ADV) in the mud and filth of the (2 ADJ) streets, or ran laughing (ADV) between the (ADJ) shanties and (2 ADJ) hovels that littered the (ADJ) hillside like the cast-off rubbish of a (ADJ) giant.

(5) The (ADJ) cat sat (ADV) licking its (ADJ) whiskers beside the fire. Its eyes moved (ADV) from person to person, fixing each with a (ADJ) stare before passing on in its own time to the next. Then it rose (ADV), stretched itself with (ADJ) deliberation, and (ADV) stalked, like a (ADJ) tiger towards the vacant armchair, into which it jumped with a (ADJ) bound.

(6) Over the (ADJ) town towered the (ADJ) cranes of the (ADJ) shipyard. Once the (ADJ) street had rung to the (ADJ) sound of hammer on steel. Now a (ADJ) hulk brooded in its rust above the (ADJ) houses of those who had built her so (ADV) but would never finish her. They, the makers, did not raise their (ADJ) faces to look on the (ADJ) gravestone of their hopes.

(60)

(b) This exercise is of the same sort. In each passage you should insert *ten* adjectives or adverbs, with the aim of making the passage more descriptive and interesting. There is one slight difference, however. This time you are not told where to put the words. It is up to you.

(1) There was a silence, then Mr Lowell got up and began to pace the room. He paused and lit his pipe. He wore his usual jacket and trousers, and an air of confusion. After a puff or two at the pipe he looked down at his visitors in their armchairs, smiled, and began to speak.

(2) The dress she wore had seen better days, but she contrived to wear it with the dignity of a lady entertaining her guests at a mansion. The guests themselves were a collection of people, all of whom carried themselves with the same faded gentility as their hostess. In the lamplight it might have been another place and age.

(3) She sat behind a desk, her fingers drumming on its surface, her gaze fixed on the middle distance. If she was listening to his explanation, she showed no sign of it, and when he paused her glance convinced him at once that pretence was useless. The arrival of this extraordinary woman had changed things for everyone.

(30)

FACTSHEET NINE

While you, as a trainee writer, may suffer from an adjective famine, professional writers — novelists, journalists, even authors of text books — have a tendency towards large adjective surpluses. They rather like what are called "purple passages" where adjectives and adverbs, metaphors and similes tumble over each other in profusion — or confusion. Sometimes it works, and the writing is very vivid and striking; sometimes it does not, and the writing becomes flowery or pompous — and boring. Let's look at a "purple passage":—

"*Vast, empty* chambers echoed *sonorously* with the *strange, deep-throated* notes of *some sepulchral* organ *remote* in the *cavernous* and *unfathomable* depths *below. Cautious, afraid, knowing well* that they were beyond *all human* help, the *benighted* travellers crept *forward, trapped* within the *pale* circle of *their misty* and *uncertain* torchlight, *blind* to the *unutterable* horrors that waited, *silent* and *hungry, close* beyond its *flickering* rim."

There are thirty adjectives and adverbs in this short passage from a horror story — and only fourteen nouns and verbs. Whether or not you *like* this style (and most people would think that it goes too far in the use of adjectives and adverbs) it does definitely manage to create an impression — to set the scene the author wants. Look what happens when we go over it with an 'Adjective-Vacuum', which sucks up all adjectives and adverbs:—

"The chambers echoed with the notes of an organ in the depths. Beyond help the travellers crept on within the circle of torchlight amidst the horrors that waited outside its rim."

It is a matter of opinion, but this also seems to work quite well in setting the scene and creating an impression. Though it is (almost) without adjectives and adverbs, it uses *appropriate* nouns and verbs to produce its effect — in the way you learnt when we looked at how to use the right synonym.

But we would probably achieve the best effect with a balanced passage, neither a rocky desert of nouns and verbs, nor a swirling sea of adjectives and adverbs. (How would you describe the second half of the sentence you have just read? Did you notice it was a metaphor?) Our end result, then, might be something of this sort:—

"*Vast, empty* chambers echoed with the notes of an organ, *remote* in the *cavernous* depths. Beyond *human* help the travellers crept on, *trapped* within the circle of torchlight, *blind* to the horrors that waited beyond its *flickering* rim."

We now have a manageable eight adjectives; not so many that we are swamped by them and they lose their effect by repetition, not so few that the description begins to lose its effect through lack of detail.

What you may not have noticed is that even the very short version of the passage — with hardly an adjective or adverb to its name — still makes use of descriptive phrases and clauses. There is an adverbial phrase of manner, "with the notes of an organ", and another of place, "in the depths", both modifying *echoed*. "Beyond help" is an adjectival phrase describing *travellers*, and "within the circle of torchlight" another adverbial phrase of place. "Amidst the horrors", "that waited", and "outside its rim" are all additional pieces of description. Take them away, and we are left not so much with the bare bones of the passage as merely its spinal column:— "The chambers echoed. The travellers crept on."

The point is this: adjectival and adverbial phrases and clauses can often be used to introduce the descriptions we want. They are a more subtle (= 'fine' or 'delicate') way of doing so than by piling up adjectives and adverbs. They are less likely to overwhelm the reader, and by using them in combination with adjectives, adverbs, a range of synonyms and a few suitable similes and metaphors, you can give your writing a great deal of variety and interest.

(a) Go over the following purple passages with an Adjective-Vacuum (the type that works for adverbs as well), and remove *all* the adjectives and adverbs from each. Write out the result. — Then make up your own mind whether it is an improvement or not.

(1) Solitary through the silent glen the searching, snuffling badger makes its wandering way, weary after a long night's dark eventful hunt. It strains its dim eyes, half blind in the spreading daylight, warily watching from side to side. It sniffs at the strong sharp scents of dewy dawn, then scurries, safe now, into the shadowy, secret, welcoming home, to wait dreaming through the dreary day till the soft grey velvet of midnight's curtains closes again over the sleeping world.

(15)

(2) The silver-speckled crests of long, coiled waves unwound into the liquid sunlight of the molten lagoon, became swirling ropes of gold and then sank into the golden waters where the heat haze hung shimmering in the air above the fiery crucible of evening.

(5)

(3) The whirling, bubbling, dancing, dipping shapes that leapt eccentrically, spun convulsively, laughed like loons, or ghoul- or ghost- or witch-faced grimaced at me, these it was who caught me up, small and wary, dull and dumpy, into their red-nosed, green-haired playabout jollity as the gaudy carnival shocked its way through the sniffing suburban streets.

(10)

(b) You may have felt that once you had vacuumed number (3), there was not a great deal left. This time, in each of these two passages you can leave just TEN adjectives and/or adverbs. It is up to you which ones are necessary, useful or vivid and striking; and which we could well manage without. (You can leave out 'and' and 'but' as necessary).

(1) Staring full upon them, red-eyed and hideous, its cavernous saw-toothed mouth a yawning, gaping pit of unspeakable horror, the fiendish and gruesome creature stood slavering in front of them inexorably barring the way on the grim and terrible path they must soon tread. The valiant, intrepid adventurers halted abruptly, fearful of its stupendous, vast, looming immensity. Karandar hesitantly drew his trusty rune-carved sword, knowing full well that it would be little use against the huge, ghoulish monstrosity from the dark unfathomable void before the beginning of time.

(15)

(2) The delicate, rueful song of the darting birds filtered softly through the lace curtains of her little first-floor apartment overlooking the Rue St. Germain. Mingled scents of lilac and drowsy honeysuckle wafted gently through open windows on a whispering whispy breeze. The sounds of the roaring traffic and the busy workaday city were muted and distant. The acrid fumes of the uncountable cars were banished. Those little breezes were come from a cool, sweet country beyond, like late but welcome messengers of times long past but always held in memory.

(15)

When you are doing these exercises, do think about the passages, and how they can be improved, and how by using the same methods your own writing can also be improved. When you realise something is bad (like number (1) in (b)), try to work out WHY it is bad, — and then avoid making the same mistake yourself!

DESCRIPTION (3)

On this sheet we will sum up what we have done so far. As you may have noticed, it has all been about how to use words. We have looked at how to get the right word, the use of descriptive words and phrases, and description by simile and metaphor. What it all comes down to is this:—

To make the words and phrases we use EFFECTIVE and SUITABLE.

Effective means that the words do the job we want and produce the right results. *Suitable* means that they are the right words for a particular piece of writing ("the context"), and they fit in with the rest of the passage.

A word can be very striking and effective in producing a particular impression, — but if it is not a suitable word that impression may be the wrong one. Look at the use of the word *grin* in this example:—

"Mrs Porter carefully replaced the antique silver teapot, and passed the delicate china cup to Felicity with a pleasant grin of encouragement on her old, finely-featured face."

A *grin* is a sort of smile — and gives an immediate impression to a reader; it is an effective description, — but here it is the *wrong* description. We want *smile* or possibly *beam*. Elderly ladies with antique silver, delicate china, and friends called Felicity just do not *grin*. In front of 'grin' is a word which is suitable, in that it fits with the rest of the sentence, but completely ineffective:— *pleasant* is one of those words like *nice* which is rapidly losing any meaning it once had. So we can either replace it with a word that actually means something specific (*polite*, or *genteel; gracious* perhaps, or *sympathetic* — all of which would add a little to the *meaning* of what we are saying). Alternatively, we might decide that it is not really needed at all, — and apply the famous Adjective-Vacuum.

The same rule applies to the similes and metaphors we use. To be effective as comparisons they will usually need to be original, or at least not in such constant use that they have become clichés. The common or clichéd expression often fails on grounds of suitability:—

"I have compared your homework, boy, with that of Jones, and I am able to inform you that both inadequate attempts are as alike as two peas in a pod."

The simile here does not fit the occasion very well. It is doubtful whether this speaker would have used one at all, probably preferring the simple adjective "identical". If he had used one, it would have been more serious, or more sarcastic ("as alike as the grubby finger marks on the covers of your two exercise books" which is more the sort of phrase a schoolmaster would use; not only more suitable but also more effective).

It is worth noticing that one of the easiest mistakes to make with similes and metaphors is exaggeration:—

"Wesley's punch hit me on the nose like a submarine-launched, enemy nuclear missile exploding."

The comparison is hardly original or interesting; its exaggeration is rather like piling up adjectives:—

"Wesley's gigantic, iron-fisted, violent punch hit me on the nose."

A single adjective would do; the pile of three adjectives loses effectiveness by going too far. Remember that adjectival or adverbial clauses often serve better than lists of adjectives, and are often a good deal more precise and informative in the description they provide:—

"The punch that Wesley swung came from low down, with the full force of his muscular arm, and hit me on the nose like a wet sandbag in flight . . ."

(a) In each of the following sentences insert a simile. Try to be original and effective in your choice of words, but also make sure the simile is suitable. Use as many words as you need (though too many will not be so effective).

    (1)   The airliner hit the mountainside like a ....
    (2)   In the house next door the baby was howling like ....
    (3)   Like .... the fighters lurched against each other, too tired to punch.
    (4)   The face that grinned at me with blackened, cracked teeth was as evil as ....
    (5)   As slowly as .... he edged round the wall, wary of even the slightest sound.
    (6)   Your handwriting, Timothy, is like ....
    (7)   As sure as .... the forces of law and order were closing in on me.
    (8)   The party was as dull as .... till Jimmy arrived with the meringues.
    (9)   He addressed his unfortunate pupils like ....
    (10) Her face shone like .... as she read quickly through the letter.

(20)

(b) In each of the following you have no more than the bare bones of a sentence. Insert adjectival or adverbial phrases and clauses that are effective and suitable to complete the sentences.

    (1)   The load which .... with .... was one which ....   (3)
    (2)   The shouts and cries of .... echoed through .... that ....   (3)
    (3)   Without .... she took the hand of .... and led him out of ....   (3)
    (4)   Amidst .... I grasped my rifle and fired foolishly at .... which ....   (3)
    (5)   .... she leaned ...., took the pencil, and drew .... the outline ....   (4)
    (6)   The master .... gazed ...., banged his staff .... and began to speak   (4)

(20)

(c) Replace each of the adjectives and adverbs in italics in the following sentences with adjectival or adverbial phrases and clauses (which can include metaphors and similes, by the way). You may well need to rewrite the sentences completely or to use more than one sentence. Make sure your versions keep the sense of all the original adjectives, and remember:— SUITABLE and EFFECTIVE!

    (1)   The *driving, numbing, lashing* force of the snow struck the travellers on the pass.   (3)
    (2)   It was an *old, wizened, thin-faced, shuffling* man who now approached us.   (4)
    (3)   The *echoing, deafening, thunderous* crash filled the small room where we waited.   (3)
    (4)   Enthralled, we watched the *miraculous* and *spectacularly brilliant* performance of the magician.   (3)
    (5)   They found that they had volunteered for a *difficult, dangerous* and *disagreeable* mission.   (3)
    (6)   *Hopelessly, diffidently, grim* and *silent,* the long line of people shuffled towards their fate.   (4)

(20)

(d) Make up a single metaphor to cover each of the following descriptions. Do *not* go immediately for the most obvious, go for the most effective.

    (1)   A large, hairy, ugly, stupid man.
    (2)   A small, slight, slim, delicate woman.

    (EXTRA QUESTION: What would you have put for these two if (1) had been *woman* and (2) had been *man?*)

    (3)   A dark, grey-green, rotting, gelatinous, vegetable mass.
    (4)   A sudden unexpected, welcome, marvellous event.
    (5)   A long, tedious, dull and boring performance.

(10)

FACTSHEET ELEVEN

SENTENCE LENGTH

The way we put words together can be as important as the words themselves. We have already seen how the use of adjectival and adverbial clauses and phrases can improve the descriptive quality of a sentence, — and do it more effectively than piling up adjectives. Now we are going to look at an even more basic element in how we construct our sentences — their length. When children first begin to write stories, they tend to use very short sentences:—

"I went out of the house. I was going to the park. I took my ball. I kicked it down the road. I chased it."

This sort of thing is very repetitive, and so tends to be rather boring. The most obviously tedious part of it is that every sentence starts with the same word — *I*. An easy rule to remember, but a good one to stick to would be:— "Try to ensure that every sentence starts in a different way". If you really must have the same subject for two consecutive main verbs, then try to find two different ways of saying it, or simply find a synonym.

So, what does our imaginary young child learn next? Teacher will probably tell him or her to join the sentences together, — usually with unfortunate results:—

"I went out of the house and I was going to the park and I took my ball and I kicked it down the road and I chased it."

One of the reasons that this sort of thing happens is that young children tend to write ACTION rather than description. In the examples we have just seen there is virtually no descriptive element. We have a list of events, and all lists tend to be boring. In an essay or story they can also be surprisingly uninformative. Remember that you are trying to give the reader a particular impression, and to do so properly you need to set the scene. We can improve our imaginary child's writing enormously by adding descriptive words and phrases. (It may even be whole sentences.) In the following version the additional descriptions are shown in italics:—

"I went *hurrying* out of the house. *It was a dull autumn day with a cold wind blowing, but it was also a Saturday,* and I was going to the park *instead of school*. I took my *old, battered* football with me and, *as I always did*, kicked it *gleefully* down the road *between the rows of parked or abandoned cars. Ignoring the disapproving glance of the man next door,* I chased *madly* after it, *the wind catching my tattered, buttonless coat as I ran.*"

All the action is still there, but suddenly we have quite a vivid picture of the scene as well. The action comes alive because of the description, and interest is added to what sounded, in the earlier versions, a fairly dull sequence of events. Once again it is a matter of *effectiveness*. Short, snappy sentences certainly can be effective. They speed up the pace of your writing, and are ideal for sudden bursts of action amid longer, descriptive sentences, as in this passage:—

"We came to a great, empty chamber lined with columns that vanished into the dark spaces of the roof. A solitary chandelier provided the only illumination, its candles guttering in the wind that stole past the ancient window panes. Like a snake striking he came at me out of the shadows. I saw him too late. A flame of pain seared into my side. I cried out. My sword dropped with a clatter. His blade flashed again. Somehow I twisted aside. He paused, breathing heavily, and we eyed each other, there in the half light, the stones of the floor already stained with the glittering black droplets of my blood."

After the two long descriptive sentences setting the scene, we have a burst of action indicated by the short rushing sentences. Then, when the action *pauses*, so does the pace of the sentences. So the lesson is this:— Use short sentences for action — but use them in combination with longer descriptive sentences. Remember the words this book started with — "Variety is the spice of life". By varying the length of your sentences and the pace of your writing, keep the reader's interest.

Here are some short passages as written by children considerably younger than yourselves. Your job (as you may have guessed already) is to improve them by adding description. You should not only be inserting adjectives and adverbs where appropriate, but also similes and metaphors; descriptive phrases and clauses; and even additional sentences. Remember to start each sentence in a different way if you can. Also try to decide in advance what impression you want to give to your reader. Then remember:— everything you include should be *effective* and *suitable*.

(1)   I arrived at the park. I was playing there. I kicked my ball against a tree. I saw Lisa. She was walking the dog. I called her. She came over. She brought Fang with her.

(2)   She got dressed and looked out of the window and then she went downstairs and she went into the kitchen and she had her breakfast and she had toast and cornflakes.

(3)   Tony knocked on the door. He waited. Then he heard a voice. He opened the door. He went inside.

(4)   Mandy was riding her bike. She saw Sharon. She waved at her. She called out to her. She did not see Mrs Kropotkin. She was crossing the road. Mandy rode straight into her. The shopping went flying. Mandy went flying too. She landed on Mrs Kropotkin. Mrs Kropotkin sat down heavily. She sat on the eggs.

(5)   It started to rain. We went into the cave. Douglas wanted to go deeper in. Bradley didn't want to. We had a vote on it. So we went on into the cave. We went a long way. Stuart had a torch. James fell over a rock. He banged into Stuart and Stuart dropped the torch. It went out.

(6)   They were going to the beach. They walked across the sand-dunes. They got changed. They ran down to the sea. They swam out to the rocks. Then they had a race back. Ella won, Jane was second, and Peter was last.

(7)   The travellers entered the room. They could see the door at the far end. There was a figure in the way. They approached it. It moved in a strange way. They could see it was not human. It was blocking their way. They had no choice. They prepared to fight it.

(8)   He ran down the left wing. He dodged two defenders. He nearly slipped. Then he regained his balance. The crowd roared. He swerved again. He was past the last defender. He shot at goal. The keeper dived. He missed. The ball hit the back of the net.

(9)   We sat down at the table. Miss Dobson spoke first. Everyone listened. She stopped and then she sat down. We all clapped. Everybody seemed to agree with her. Miss Dobson smiled at all the people. I did not agree with her, though. I frowned. I noticed she did not smile at me.

(10) Elaine was talking to Billy and Sam. Then they went out of the room. Simon followed them. They went down the corridor. They looked back. Simon hid. They did not see him. He went on following. They went out through the door. They went into the playground. Then they went down to the games hut. They looked around. Simon pretended to be playing. They went into the shed. They closed the door. Simon crept up. He listened. They were whispering. He looked through a window. He saw them. They were kneeling down. They had a box. They were looking into it. They all began to talk now. Now Simon could hear what they said.

(70 — 7 each)

23

FACTSHEET TWELVE

SYNTHESIS OF SENTENCES (1)

In the last Factsheet we were a little ironic about the teacher's instruction to join short sentences together. (What does 'ironic' mean? If you are not sure, look it up!). In fact it is good advice if you know how to do it properly.

There are various sorts of sentences:—

SIMPLE — with one main verb.

DOUBLE (OR MULTIPLE) — with two (or more) main verbs, joined by conjunctions like *and, but, or* etc.

COMPLEX — with one or more main verb, but also subordinate clauses . (Subordinate clauses are basically pieces of additional information or description introduced by words such as:— *who, which, that; when, as, if, although.*)

We will start by looking at how to join short simple sentences to produce double or multiple sentences. (Complex sentences await you in the next Factsheet!)

Joining sentences ("synthesis") can be quite effectively done by the use of the simple conjunctions, including the dreaded *and.* The resulting double or multiple sentences very often do their job better than a series of short sentences (unless of course you want short sentences for a purpose). In particular when you have two verbs, one after the other, with the same subject, do not give them separate sentences:—

"We went down the road. Then we turned into the High Street" is better as

"We went down the road and then turned into the High Street."

First Warning:— Be careful when using 'then' as a conjunction.

"We went down the road, then we turned into the High Street" is not very good English.

We can do much the same combining three separate sentences:—

"We opened our books. We turned to page twenty-four. We began to read" becomes

"We opened our books, turned to page twenty-four and began to read."

Notice that in multiple sentences like this there is a *comma* but no *and* at the first join. You can also have a *comma* in front of the final *and* if you want to emphasize the break a little more; otherwise it is usual to do without.

Second Warning:— Try to avoid long multiple sentences where there are more than three main verbs. Also, do try to use other conjunctions apart from *and;* even *but* can be a welcome change.

It is very often sensible to combine sentences which, though they have different subjects, are still obviously closely connected with each other:—

"The teacher told us to turn to page twenty-four. We began to read" becomes

"The teacher told us to turn to page twenty-four, *and* we began to read."

"We saw Mrs Lumpfish. Unfortunately, she saw us too."

"We saw Mrs Lumpfish and unfortunately she saw us too."

"I kicked the ball. It flew into the road. A car ran straight over it."

"I kicked the ball, it flew into the road, and a car ran straight over it."

In all of these, the double or multiple sentences read better than the very short simple ones. Pieces of brief description or minor action often do not need a separate sentence of their own, and can be attached to a simple or multiple sentence as a phrase. A phrase, unlike a clause, has no verb of its own, though phrases can be introduced by the adjectives formed from verbs called participles (often ending in *ing* or *ed*), — or by prepositions:—

"I was going to work today. I saw a strange sight" becomes

"Going to work today, I saw a strange sight." (*Going* is a present participle).

Third Warning:— Be careful where you put the participle —

"I saw a strange sight going to work today" is NOT what you mean.

"I saw a strange sight on my way to work today" is an alternative combination using a preposition. Similarly:—

"He gave a cry. He attacked me" can become "With a cry, he attacked me."

If you can do without a particular verb altogether, by all means do so:—

"He ran down the road. He was furious. He was chasing us" becomes:—

"He chased us furiously down the road." We need neither *was* nor *ran* to preserve the meaning and combine the three sentences into one.

(a) Combine these simple sentences into double or multiple (not complex) sentences. Use the conjunctions which seem most appropriate. Try to get the commas right. (You can leave out *then,* and make other minor changes you may need.)

(1)   He leaned back. Then he yawned widely.
(2)   She opened the door. She looked out into the garden.
(3)   You cut along this line. Then you fold it down here. Then you glue it together.
(4)   We saw the faint light. We cheered aloud. We ran towards it.
(5)   She took careful aim. The rifle shook in her hands.
(6)   Take a left at the post office. Go along New Street. You'll see it in front of you.
(7)   Holmes sighed. He fingered his pipe. Then he put it down.
(8)   We saw the caretaker. He did not see us. We were able to hide.
(9)   He looked out of the window. It was raining. There was no taxi in sight.
(10) Miss Snooks told Jenny to open the door. She got up to do it. Then she tripped over.

(20)

(b) Combine these sentences. For each question produce TWO answers, one in which the combination is done by the use of a *participle,* the other in which it is done by using a *preposition* and phrase. Each sentence should have just one finite verb. (Clue: "I was *going* down the road" — finite verb; "*Going* down the road, I saw a strange sight" — participle.)

(1)   I ran for my life. I was terrified.
(2)   I gave a sudden gasp. I jumped up from my chair.
(3)   She sniffed contemptuously. Then she flounced out.
(4)   Carter was listening to the news. He expected the worst.
(5)   Sheila wrote him a letter. In it she told him of her forthcoming marriage.

(20)

(c) Combine the following sentences. For each question produce a single *simple* sentence. You may find that the verbs in some of the original sentences can be eliminated altogether.

(1)   The evening was dark. We could hardly see.
(2)   There was a great roar and a flash. The lightning struck the tree.
(3)   The plane rushed downwards through the air. It hurtled towards the ground. Then it crashed into the mountainside.
(4)   I did not stop to think about it. I handed over the money.
(5)   We raced towards the cliff. There was an overhang of rocks. It was pouring with rain. We were desperate for shelter.

(10)

(d) The following passage needs some sentence combination, but not too much. You may combine simple sentences into double or multiple sentences. Alternatively you may eliminate some sentences by using descriptive phrases or words. Where you think that the shorter sentences are more appropriate keep them. You should end with about fifteen sentences.

"The wind roared. It sounded like a hungry beast. The waves smashed against the ship's side. They battered at the rusty plates. They washed over the decks. We were running before the storm. We could see almost nothing. Night was closing in. It added to the terror. Then we saw it. It was coming at us out of the howling gloom. It was heading towards us. It drove in on our port side. The courses converged. The white bulk towered above us. It struck. The ice ripped into the ship's side. Metal tore. It was like paper. The ship listed. It went further and further over. Men slid down the decks. There were screams and cries. They added to the scream of ice on iron. Then the iceberg was gone. It had vanished into the darkness. It was lost in the storm. It left a sinking ship behind."

(20)

FACTSHEET THIRTEEN

SYNTHESIS OF SENTENCES (2)

Complex sentences are those which have a main verb and other verbs *dependent* on it in clauses of their own (sometimes known as *subordinate* clauses).

They can be ADJECTIVAL CLAUSES, in which case they will be describing a noun or pronoun. These are normally introduced (= 'started') by a relative pronoun — *who, whom, whose, which, that* (and hence are sometimes called *relative* clauses). The relative clause is a very convenient way of combining two sentences:—

"She was wearing the new dress. She had just bought it" becomes

"She was wearing the new dress which she had just bought."

You will sometimes find relative clauses in which the relative pronoun itself is missed out. In this example we could have written:— "She was wearing the new dress she had just bought." Only miss out the relative pronoun if the result still makes good sense.

Another warning: You can have too much of a good thing. Two relative clauses in one sentence can often sound clumsy. Think about this example:—

"The boy kicked the ball. It broke the window. The boy ran away" could be re-written as "The boy *who* kicked the ball *which* broke the window ran away."

ADVERBIAL CLAUSES have more different types, and are introduced by a wide variety of words.

Here are some examples of the many possibilities, all of which can add variety to your work:—

"I saw Mr Jones. He was coming after me. Then I ran for it" becomes
"*When* I saw Mr Jones coming after me, I ran for it."

Notice that as well as the adverbial clause of TIME introduced by *when*, we have also managed to reduce the sentence 'He was coming after me' to the phrase 'coming after me'. Clauses of time, which tell the order of events, are very useful in combining sentences. They can be introduced by many words, for example — *after, as soon as, while, before, until.*

"He was running. It is forbidden to run here" becomes
"He was running *where* it is forbidden." This is an adverbial clause of PLACE.

"I wanted to be able to see. I climbed the fence" can become a clause of PURPOSE or REASON:—
"I climbed the fence so that I would be able to see' (*purpose*), or
"I wanted to be able to see, so I climbed the fence" (*reason*).

These sorts of adverbial clauses, which you can also introduce with *as, because, in order to* etc., are also very convenient and simple ways of joining sentences.

"It was a difficult decision. Only I could make it" becomes
"*Although* it was a difficult decision, only I could make it."
Clauses introduced by *although, as if,* and *even if* are known as CONCESSIVE clauses.

Notice the alternative double sentence we could have made by combining the two in this example:—
"It was a difficult decision, *but* only I could make it."

You will perhaps be able to see the difference between a double sentence and a complex sentence more clearly if you compare these two results. In the 'although' version, the clause beginning with 'although' cannot really exist by itself; it is *dependent* on the rest of the sentence. In the second version we could let the half beginning with *but* stand by itself as a separate sentence; it would not be perfect English, but it would still make sense.

When you are combining two or more sentences in this way to make a complex sentence, try to keep the most important piece of action or description as the main clause of the sentence, and make the less important items depend on it:—

"I saw him walking along the gangway. Then I drew my gun. Then I shot him" becomes
"*As soon as* I saw him walking along the gangway, I drew my gun and shot him."

This is better than the alternative version:—
"I saw him walking along the gangway *before* I drew my gun and shot him."

Both use adverbial clauses of time, but in the alternative version the *shooting* is subordinate to (and therefore seems less important than) the *seeing*. In real life you would expect the shooting to be the main event, so make sure that is how it appears when you write about it.

Notice that a subordinate clause may well come *before* the main clause in a sentence (as in the first version of this example, beginning with *as soon as*).

Notice also that there is much to be said for using both a subordinate clause and two main clauses joined by a simple *and* or *but* in the same longer sentence. It adds variety to your writing; and the more varied techniques you use, the more likely your reader will stay awake.

(a) Combine these sentences using adjectival (relative) clauses:—

   (1) We were waiting for Veronica. As usual, she was late.

   (2) I glanced down the street. It was narrow and dirty.
       (*Note:* you need to think which half of the combined sentence should be the main clause, and which the subordinate clause).

   (3) I climbed the stairs. At the top stood my mother.

   (4) We have made the decision. Puddick will have to go.

   (5) The boy put his hand up. It was his book.

   (6) The men laughed and waved when they saw us. We had been sent to kill them.

   (7) She was hanging out the washing. A sudden gust of wind caught it. A moment before the sheet had been clean. Now it was flapping across the muddy potato patch.
       (Make *two* sentences of of these four — Four marks.)

   (8) I read that article. It was in a magazine. You gave me the magazine. The article was very interesting.
       (Make *one* sentence out of these four — Four marks.)

                                                                                                            (20)

(b) Combine these sentences using adverbial clauses. In each case a clue is given you as to which type of clause you could use. (If you can do it using a different adverbial clause, you may do so.)

   (1) The cliff was very high. He had no choice but to jump.   (Concessive clause.)

   (2) The clock struck twelve. At that moment I saw the shadowy shape beginning to form in front of me.
                                                                                            (Clause of time.)

   (3) Jerry forced the door of the generator house. He wanted to discover if the American was still inside.
                                                                                   (Clause of reason or purpose.)

   (4) There he was, waiting for me on the quayside. I had least expected him there.   (Clause of place.)

   (5) He travelled by car to Berlin. I took the train, and made the journey more quickly. (Clause of comparison; there is no example on the Factsheet, so you will have to exercise your brain in deciding what key word usually introduces such a clause.)

                                                                                                            (10)

(c) Once again, combine these sentences by using adverbial clauses. This time there are no clues provided.

   (1) You must throw your gun out first. Then I am prepared to hand over the girl.

   (2) You have always said Joanne was not very bright. She has shown you up this time, Bill.

   (3) "I hit him a few times with the crowbar, m'lud. He was getting on my nerves."

   (4) Mary came out of the cabin. I recognized her at once. We had not seen each other for ten years.
                                                                                            (One sentence).
                                                                                                            (10)

(d) Combine the sentences in this passage into TEN, or fewer. Do not make your sentences too long and clumsy. You can use any method you like, but you are rationed to ONE extra *and*.

> She began to climb. She was afraid. Heights had always terrified her. The cliff was steep. It was also rough and jagged. There were many footholds. There were some bad places. The rocks were slippery. It had been raining. She slipped once. Afterwards she was even more careful. She did not look down. She did not dare. She knew it would only make her dizzy. She concentrated on the top. It was tantalizingly near now. She felt she could almost grasp it. The last part was the most difficult. There were fewer crevices. The face became more sheer. Her fingers were torn and bleeding. She clutched desperately at the last hold. It was a rock. It jutted out. It was only a yard below the summit. The rock came away in her hand.

                                                                                                            (30)

FACTSHEET FOURTEEN

NARRATIVE FORM (1)

Many or most of the essays and compositions you are asked to write will be of the narrative kind. In effect all this means is that is that you have to write a straightforward story. A story will have:—

Events following each other in natural progression from one to the next

From a clear starting point

To a definite ending.

This sort of composition is probably the easiest to write, and in a test or exam where you are given a choice of titles it is *safest* to pick one which can be written as a narrative. Here are some titles (based on examples from examination papers) which are inviting a narrative:—

An Unexpected meeting	*A Day of Disasters*	*Suddenly I Found Myself Invisible*
Night Train	*Appointment with Danger*	*A Journey I Would Rather Forget*
The Practical Joke	*A Horse's Tale*	*The Door I Was Told Not To Open*

There is also a whole range of titles beginning: "Imagine you are . . . .", and another range of compositions where you are given the first sentence or sentences of a story and have to take it on from there. (Be careful with this last sort; it is often harder than you might think to fit in with the style of the opening you are given.)

A narrative will contain a great deal of action.

On the other hand it must not be *all* action. If it is, your reader will be swamped by the speed of events and lose track of things, — and you will be at the end of the story almost as soon as you have started.

You already know how important it is to include description in your writing. Every piece of background detail you include will make your story seem far more real to your reader. In some stories you may even want to start with a description, to set the scene of the action. Be careful, though, if you do this. A great deal of flowery description right at the start before anything happens may well bore or irritate people who want to get on with the story.

In general, however, if you mix description with action your writing will be more interesting to read. Remember the other 'tricks of the trade' you have already learnt as well. Vary your sentence length, and use different forms of description — phrases and clauses, similes and metaphors — as well as simple adjectives and adverbs.

Narrative stories are nearly always invented. With any sort of *fiction* the writer's first job is to persuade the reader to believe in it. Even though it is not true, you must try to make it *seem* true. Good background description will help a very great deal to do this. What will not help to make the story believable is too much exaggeration. You already know the dangers of going 'over the top' with your descriptions.

The same applies to the events you make happen in your story. Even if you have set the adventure in the wilds of the South American forests or on the far side of the moon, what happens must still seem at least *possible*. On the whole, so long as the events follow naturally from each other, and the description is good, most things can be made believable.

Your aim is to be original and unusual — but not to be ridiculous. One rampaging space-monster may be possible; two are less likely; three are beginning to sound a bit silly. It is better in fact to do without the monsters altogether. You will find the real world and real people easier to describe, because you already know them. Stories set in city streets can be as exciting and interesting as stories set amid the stars.

(a) Copy down the following list of essay titles and instructions. Next to each one which you could easily write as a narrative story, put the word *narrative*. Do not try to stretch the title too far from its natural meaning.

(1) Autumn Leaves.

(2) A Day to Remember.

(3) A Terrible Disappointment.

(4) The Toy Shop; write a story about what you would see on a visit to a toy shop.

(5) My Favourite Lessons.

(6) The Face at the Window.

(7) Discuss the advantages and disadvantages of having a prefect system at school.

(8) Was it a mistake to abolish the death penalty for murder?

(9) Looking After Little Brother Sammy.

(10) Describe the job of *either* an airline pilot *or* a fashion designer.

(11) Write a review of a (fictional) book you have read recently.

(12) Moving House.

(13) Imagine you are a glass marble. Describe your life and adventures.

(14) The advantages of learning science at school.

(15) My Home. Write a description of the house or flat where you live and the people you share it with.

(16) Inside the Television.

(17) Collecting as a Hobby.

(18) Write a composition beginning:—

> "The table seemed larger, and the chair too. My feet were not touching the ground any more. My clothes were hanging loosely on me. . . . . . ."

(19) The Statue that Spoke.

(20) Write a composition based on these lines of poetry, or the ideas and images contained in them:—

> "Day after day, day after day,
> We stuck; nor breath nor motion;
> As idle as a painted ship
> Upon a painted ocean."

                                                                                                    (20)

(b) For each of the titles which you have said it is possible to write as a narrative composition, explain, briefly, in a few sentences, what sort of story you had in mind. Give a brief idea of what might happen in your story, — but do not start writing it!

                                                                                                    (20)

(c) Make up ten titles or sets of instructions of your own which would be good for writing as narratives.

                                                                                                    (10)

For each one, in a sentence or two outline the sort of story you would plan to write on that particular title.

                                                                                                    (20)

FACTSHEET FIFTEEN

NARRATIVE FORM (2)

As we discovered at the beginning of the last Factsheet a narrative story is first and foremost a *sequence of events*. The events make up the skeleton of the story — the bare bones which you can then cover with descriptive flesh! To turn a pile of old bones into a skeleton you need to put them together in the right way. The same applies to the sequence of events that makes up a story.

The first thing you must get right is the order of events. On the whole it is easier to tell the story in the order in which things happened. You can include *flashbacks* to earlier events; but if you do, make it very plain that this is what you are doing, do not do it very often, and then only if you have a good reason.

The second thing to get right is to avoid complications. If you were writing a novel you could have as many characters as you liked. In a short story, keep the number small. You will not be able to describe very many people, and the person reading will tend to get them mixed up. The same applies to frequent changes of scene. Try to keep the events all in much the same place — or at least in a very small number of places (such as *two*). Remember that each new scene needs to be described and made realistic for your reader; if you have only one setting for the story, you can improve on its description with little additional points all the way through it. By the end the person reading your composition will know that scene almost as well as you do, — and that is what you are aiming for.

Thirdly, decide what is important to the story, and include it; decide what is unimportant, and leave it out. This applies in particular to pieces of description. Look at this example:—

"The three of them sat down to tea. It was cream cakes, but before that they had toast and jam. Two of them had tea, but one had coffee. When they were eating they started to plan the murder. . . . ."

It is just possible that the details of the menu are necessary to the story, but it is not very likely. This is all detail we can do without: it doesn't help to set the scene for the main action (which seems to be a murder), and it doesn't get on with the story. You may also have noticed that here the writer even managed to get the order wrong when he told us that they had to eat!

On the other hand, do not leave out vital pieces of information. Look at this example:—

"I looked in through the glass doors. Mrs Hunter was not there. So we would be able to talk to Billy behind the counter. I beckoned the others and the three of us went in. Billy looked up the address for us in the delivery book without the slightest trouble. Then we were off to Barlow Street before she got back."

This is a paragraph taken complete from a story. There is no mention, before or after, of who Mrs Hunter might be, and why she was a problem. Here we do need the additional snippet of information "our old enemy, who owned the newsagents" or something similar, to help us understand what is going on.

All the three points we have considered add up to one vital point. You *must* know in advance what is going to happen in your story. You cannot start off with a vague idea, and hope the story will come to you as you go along. You will end up (possibly) with some sort of story, but it will not be a very good one. You are bound to include unnecessary things and leave out important ones if you don't know the real point of the story yourself. Your order of events may well be confused. Things will happen with no good reason, and will be unconnected. Worst of all, you may well run out of things to say, and find yourself tacking on additional events and bits and pieces of description in order to make up space or fill up the time available.

On this Worksheet the questions are all about the following passage. It is taken from the middle of a story written by a clever but disorganized twelve year-old. Three children are trying to lever an ancient millstone out of the ground and bring it down a hill to their village. There they plan to sell it to a collector of antiques who has just arrived in the district. The whole story centres around the stone and their efforts to get it. You might like to know that the story is set in India.

> "Gopal put his full weight on the iron tube. He had at last managed to get it underneath. Meena and Vishni pulled at the edges with their fingers. Now they were managing to get a grip. It was starting to come loose. The stone was half buried in the ground. The grass had been growing right up onto the top of it. They were all tired from the effort. The combined strength of all three of them was moving it, though. It came slowly up till it stood on its broad rim. So now they could have a rest. They sat down under the tree. It was a long time since they had eaten and they were hungry. Fortunately Vishni had brought some of the little cakes that her mother had baked in the morning. They were very nice. Then they got up and went back to the stone. It was a metre across and rough and chipped. But they could see the old carved letters on it more clearly now. The light was striking it at a different angle, you see. Gopal pushed the battered rusty tube through. He took one end and the two girls took the other. Now they were ready to start rolling it down the hill."

(1)   Make a list of the events, and other major pieces of information and description, in what you think should be the correct order. The order in the passage is rather confused, so you will need to do some reorganization.

(20)

(2)   At least one important piece of information or description is missing from the passage. Make a note of the additional things you would want to include in this part of the story to help the reader. (There has already been a description of the three children and their village in the first paragraphs, so do not include this.)

(10)

(3)   As well as the omission of some useful information, and one piece of necessary information, you may well feel that the writer has included some things that are not really necessary at all for this story. Note down the items that you would leave out in order to speed up the action.

(10)

(4)   Now try to rewrite the paragraph — with the order improved, the additional information you needed put in, and what is not necessary left out. You may also want to insert one or two pieces of description to help provide the background scene. (For example, from the passage as written it is not clear that it is set in India.)

(30)

(5)   List the events, together with information and description, you think would be needed in the first two paragraphs of the story — the paragraphs that came before this one. Check what you are told about them in the introduction — and in question 2 — and make sure that you include this (unless you think it is not really necessary to the story!)

(20)

(6)   Write brief notes — no more than a dozen or so items — of the events which might form the basic skeleton of the rest of the story. Do they get the stone down the hill safely? Is it a hair-raising journey? Do they sell it to this strange collector? Is it really valuable? Is there some secret about it? — It is entirely up to you!

(20)

FACTSHEET SIXTEEN

ESSAY PLANS

You may well have worked out from the last Factsheet and Worksheet that it is a very good idea to make notes *before* you start an essay or composition on what you are going to put in it. These notes are your *essay plan*. An essay plan is essential to any sort of story you write. Do not try to manage without one — and that is an order. . . . . .

This is how to go about it.

Firstly, choose your title carefully (assuming you are given a choice). If you want to write a narrative, make sure the title is right. You must not try to twist the title round to make it mean something different. If the title is "My Home Town", do not write an imaginative account of adventure set in your home town on Mars, with you as a Martian, — particularly if the essay is for an exam. The people who set that title wanted a particular sort of essay (a largely descriptive one in fact). If you want to do a narrative, make sure your title is suitable for one. In your plan and your essay you must then stick to the title. Do not wander off the point. Keep the title in the front of your mind as you do the plan.

The next thing you have to do is pause and think. Think what your story is going to be, — the one or two main things that are going to happen in it. There is no useful advice for this part of the process. You are on your own. As soon as you do have an idea, jot it down in a couple of notes. This is the *theme* of your story, — what it is going to be about.

Check that it does fit the title. Then, once you have your theme, *stick to it.*

The next stage is to make a list of the main events you want to include in your story. Make sure that one follows from another, and that they do fit together. Remember, getting the order right is one of the main things to aim at.

When you are doing your plan, use a spare sheet of paper, and set it out so that you leave yourself a good deal of space (because you will think of additional things as you prepare the plan).

Each of the main events which you have now set out should be the title of a paragraph in the essay. (Do not write titles for the paragraphs when you do the essay though!) It is important to divide an essay up into paragraphs, and they should indicate the natural breaks in the progression of events. They should not be scattered about at random. If you do an essay plan, you will have your paragraphs sorted out in advance. The reason you need paragraphs is to make it easier for the reader. A whole block of continuous writing is very hard to read — a bit like a sentence with no punctuation and far too many *ands.*

Then make notes of places where you need to have descriptions in your narrative. You may even decide you need to include a whole paragraph of description. If so, you can insert it into your plan in the main list. Make it clear on your plan where you think description of places or people is important. Do not be afraid of making notes for yourself as reminders. *Tell* yourself the sort of impression you want to give.

Finally, when you are doing your plan take particular care with the notes you make on the first and last paragraphs, the beginning and ending of the story. These are so important that they each have a Factsheet of their own (Seventeen and Eighteen).

When your plan, with all its notes, is complete, read it through to make sure it makes sense, and does sound like a good story. As you check it you will probably find yourself adding extra notes.

Then turn the plan into a story!

It really is worth the time and trouble to do a proper plan. It will improve your writing a great deal.

(a) Here are the beginnings of an essay plan, once again as done by a twelve year-old. The headings for the paragraphs have been set out, together with the general theme. But there are no extra notes about descriptions and additional information. Copy out the plan, but in your version insert the additional notes that belong in the right hand column.

Title: "A Mistake on the Overnight Sleeper"

Theme: A couple of strange characters on the train — two children try to investigate them — they turn out to be detectives — the children cause chaos to their plans.

Plan:

Para 1	The two children sharing a sleeping compartment — setting the scene.	Leave enough space next to each to put in additional notes about other important things you want to include and pieces of description.
Para 2	They hear two men in the next compartment — all about a robbery.	
Para 3	They make plans, wait till the men go out, then go into their compartment.	
Para 4	They set a trap involving mailbags and luggage rack netting.	
Para 5	One man rushes in, in a hurry, and the 'net' falls on him.	
Para 6	There is a struggle, the second man comes in, and the children are captured.	
Para 7	The children accuse the men, who explain they are detectives.	
Para 8	Ending — one of the detectives says: 'And there go the real robbers' — just as the train pulls out of a station.	

(20)

You might notice three things about this plan.
(1)   The title was probably 'fishing' for a humorous essay, but since this version fits the title exactly, it is quite 'correct'.
(2)   There is no rule that everything has to 'turn out alright in the end'.
(3)   Finally, notice that your paragraph plan can have a fair amount of detail in it. How much you want to include at this stage is up to you.

(b)   This time you have to do more of the work. Here are two essay titles, and the notes on the theme of the essay. Your job is to write out the full plan for each of the titles. Set it out in the same way as the one in (a) above. You may well want to spread it over a whole page, and you should certainly write it in abbreviated or 'note' form.

(1)   *Title:* "A Holiday that Went Wrong".
       Theme: Two people on a camping holiday; after arriving by bus they camp in a pleasant quiet valley; but there is a sudden storm, the valley turns into a raging torrent, and their tents are swept away; they return home wet and bedraggled, but alive.
(2)   *Title:* "Trouble in the Street".
       Theme: A new family in the street are harassed by a group of thugs, and finally one of the family is badly hurt. The other people then band together to put a stop to it, but it is too late, and the new family move away.

(40)

(c)   This time you have the whole job to do. Here are two essay titles. For each write a complete plan, including theme, division into paragraphs and additional notes.
(1)   "On the Wrong Track"   (2)   "And then there was one. . . ."

(40)

(d)   Your final task is to go back to the completed plan you wrote for (a) on this page — and write the complete essay that goes with it!

(30)

FACTSHEET SEVENTEEN

HOW TO BEGIN

Most people think that an essay should begin with 'the introduction'. This is certainly true in essays asking you to 'discuss' something, but is much less the case when you are writing a narrative. You do not want to begin: "This is a story about . . ."

The equivalent of an introduction in a narrative is very often a paragraph in which you *set the scene* of the action. You know how important descriptive pieces are in narrative, but you do have to be careful when you start with one. A long piece of description right at the beginning before anything has happened can be rather boring, and may put the reader off.

One alternative is to jump straight into the action. This has its problems too. It may well be that you will have to come back to some of the background details you have missed out, and that means the sequence of events will be out of order. It can be done, by a *flashback* for example:—

"Above me was the long, slippery-sided shaft with a faint circle of light at the top. I sat down in despair and wondered how I could have got myself into this mess. If only I hadn't agreed to Read's dishonest little scheme. That was when it all began . . ."

Once you have come this far you can easily tell the story of how it did all begin. Not only have you caught the reader's attention by placing yourself at the bottom of a shaft, you have also made him wonder what Read's little scheme actually was. He has the incentive to read on. The two rules to observe if you do this are:—

(1) Do not make the flashback too long and complicated. Get back to the main action quickly.

(2) When you have events out of sequence like this, *plan* them very carefully before you start, so that *you* do not get confused.

What you are trying to do at the start of an essay is catch the reader's attention, so that he is interested enough to read on. So a great deal depends on the first sentence or two.

"My holiday began on a Wednesday. We set off early. We were going by car to the West Country . . ."

This is less than exciting, so let's try an alternative:—

"The first disaster of our holiday occurred in the fast lane of the M4 near Reading. We were on our way to the West Country . . ."

This is better. The reader will be wondering what the disaster was, and will be prepared to put up with a bit of necessary background in order to find out. Make sure the background you include is *necessary* though. We do not really need to know it was Wednesday, or that the car is a pretty metallic blue colour . . . Also, remember what you have already learnt about making your writing interesting by varying description with action.

A piece of description can itself catch the attention if it is striking or unusual:—

"The wriggling snake of motorway lights wound into the west before us . . ."

Even a statement of what your story is going to be about (an 'introduction') can work if you can do it in an interesting and entertaining way:—

"Our 'nice quiet holiday in the West Country' turned out to be more like a trip by wagon train to the Wild West — and through Indian country too."

This just a rather better way of saying:—

"My story is about our holiday in the West country. It was supposed to be nice and quiet, but many unexpected and unwelcome things happened to us."

Here is another way of introducing the same story interestingly:—

"Holidays are supposed to be quiet, relaxing times, when you escape from the hurly-burly of workaday life; on our holiday we wrote off the car, were (briefly) arrested, spent a night under a hedge in a cowfield, and were pursued, so we thought, by a ghost."

You do need to be careful with this approach though. You may well want to surprise your reader occasionally, so do not give away all of the story in advance.

A piece of 'snappy' dialogue or conversation can also be a good way to start:—

" 'Mum, I want to be sick,' said my little brother suddenly from the back seat."

Or alternatively:—

" 'What's that banging noise from the engine, Dad?' I asked as we pulled on to the M4."

When you do your essay *plan* and before you start writing the story itself, it is well worth devising your first sentence (or couple of sentences) in advance. You should also pay particular attention to the planning of the first paragraph as a whole. It is going to set the tone of the rest of the composition through the words you use and the sort of description you include.

So, to sum up, the rule about starting essays is a simple one:— *Catch the reader's attention.*

(a) Here are the opening sentences of five essays written by pupils aged eleven to fourteen. Copy down each of them, and then carry out each of the following tasks:—

   (i)   Say whether it is a good opening to the story or a bad one. Explain as fully as you can your reasons for your opinion.

                                                                                                  (20)

   (ii) Write your own version of the opening. — Even if you thought it was already quite good, you can surely do better. Include in your version the ideas and information provided by the original writer, but feel free to add as much as you like to them.

                                                                                                  (20)

   (1) *An Interesting Journey*
        This is a story about a really interesting time I had. It was when we went on the school trip to Calais. We went by coach and then by boat. I liked the boat best.

   (2) *The Race*
        Our street is quite long but not very wide. There are lamp-posts down both sides. You can use them as starting and finishing posts. Cars can only park on one side because there are double yellow lines on the other. We had the big race in our street.

   (3) *The Haunted House*
        The haunted house was very dark and gloomy. It was an old house and no-one had lived there for a long time. All the windows were broken, and there were weeds all over the garden. It needed painting too.

   (4) *An Unexpected Encounter*
        My unexpected encounter was with my friend, Gary Wilson, whom I had known at school, but had not seen for years. He came up to me on the corner of Southampton Street one morning and said,
        "Hallo, Lesley, I haven't seen you for ages. What a surprise!"

   (5) *No Hiding Place*
        The children were running away from their wicked stepmother, who was called Mrs Wood. She had a plan to have them put in a home. There were three of them, and their names were Terry, Lenny and Josephine. Josephine was the eldest. She was fifteen.

(b) This time you have to write your own openings for stories with the titles you are given. You should only write a few sentences for most of them. Follow the particular instructions you are given for the different titles.

   (i)   For the first three titles write a *descriptive* opening. (So your first sentence at least must be purely descriptive.)
         1. *Treasure Island.*
         2. *Imagine you are a toy in a toy cupboard. Describe your experiences and adventures.*
         3. *The Eventful Day.*

   (ii) For numbers four, five and six begin with a piece of *action* which is designed to catch the reader's attention.
         4. *Flight to Nowhere.*
         5. *The Mysterious Letter.*
         6. *What my Little Sister Did.*

The remaining questions each have their own instructions:—
         7. *Never believe what you hear.* For this title write an interesting 'introduction' telling in an original way what the story will be about.
         8. *In A Hurry.* This time begin with a piece of speech or dialogue.
         9. *Trapped.* For this title use the 'flashback' technique, either as the opening sentence itself, or immediately after your first sentence. (You may need a longer paragraph for your answer this time.)
        10. *Write an essay which begins:— "I had just sat down on the park bench. Tom had taken Patch off for a run among the trees. Baby John was feeding the ducks, safe in the care of Annie. Now I could have a rest."*
             So far in this there has been nothing much to interest the reader perhaps. See if you can get the story moving, in whatever way you choose, in the rest of the first paragraph.

                                                                                                  (40)

FACTSHEET EIGHTEEN

<u>HOW TO END</u>

If you are writing a factual essay, giving your opinions or discussing some point, then your ending will be a conclusion or *summing up*. In a narrative, in a way you also want to sum things up. You want to make the whole story seem worth telling. You want to give it some point. You need to tie up the loose ends, and explain anything that needs explaining (as is often the case in detective or mystery stories). Above all, you do not want to leave things hanging in the air, so that it isn't really clear whether you have really finished the story at all — or just run out of time, paper . . . . . or interest.

So long as you *plan* your essay, all these things should be arranged in advance. You will have your theme noted down, and while you are writing the plan you will be able to keep the ending of the story in mind, so that all the events work towards it. You must *know* the ending before you start the composition. There is something to be said for thinking of a good ending first, and then planning a story to fit it. Let's look at a few different sorts of endings:—

SUMMING UP:— Here you are trying to bring the story full circle so that you end by referring back to the title, or to what you have written about it, as in:—

"Now we would never know who had written the letter that caused us so much trouble." (Title: *The Mysterious Letter*.)

"How could anyone ever forget a day when a tree fell on the house and my baby brother was born?" (Title: *An Eventful Day*.)

It is sometimes quite a good idea to put this and other sorts of endings into the mouths of your characters, as in this example:—

" 'If that was a holiday, give me a hard day's work any time,' said Dad with a sigh." (Title: *A Holiday that Went Wrong*; you have already seen some beginnings for this title on Factsheet Seventeen.)

ENDING WITH A BANG:— Here you are trying to bring the story to a sudden or exciting end, or to end with a clever or memorable phrase that nicely concludes the action.

"So we set off home, the disasters that had comprised our holiday over at last. Were we glad! — Then the tyre burst. . . " (Title: *A Holiday that Went Wrong*, again.)

The bang does not have to be quite as literal as a bursting tyre. Look at these examples, both on the title: *Flight to Freedom*, where you might also say that the last sentences are a kind of summing up:—

"He gave a single cry. Then he fell into the darkness. He at least had found his freedom."

"I could see the wire ahead of me now. Another shot rang out and I saw the spurt of the bullet in the snow. My lungs were on fire, each breath grating in my throat. The first of the dogs reached me. I felt its teeth in my sleeve. With one last desperate wrench I ripped my coat away. Then I was there. I flung myself over the wire, ignoring the barbs. I had made it. I had escaped."

SURPRISE:— This is a variation on ending with a bang. We might call this sort of ending the 'twist in the tail'. Basically you have led the reader to think one thing all the way through the story, then you change everything round right at the end. Be careful if you try to do this. It is quite hard. — Your plan should tell you if it is going to work or not before you start writing it. Here is an example where it does work, written by a thirteen year old:—

"Somehow I forced myself to approach the hideous creature. It came nearer too, leering horribly at me. With my last dregs of courage I reached out my hand to touch its hand. My fingers met the cold, shiny glass of a mirror." (Title: *The Secret Room*.)

THE DYING FALL:— In this sort of ending you do the opposite to ending with a bang. It is the equivalent to the hero riding away into the sunset that you get in so many cowboy films. It may contain some action, but none of it vital to the story. It will probably contain a great deal of description. (The words 'dying fall' refer to the fading away of music at the end of a piece.) Here are some examples:—

"The waves broke gently over the reef, scattering their silver spray in the sunshine, all their force of the day before vanished away. No sign remained now of the tall ship that lay far beneath, hidden forever in the silence of the sea." (Title: *Shipwreck*.)

"I watched him till he reached the end of the street. I raised my hand to wave, but he did not look back. I knew I would never see him again." (Title: *Chance Encounter*.)

Any of these types of endings are effective. The things to avoid are hackneyed endings (ones that have been used too many times before), and weak endings, like "It was all over" and "We had had a very good time."

If you plan your essay properly you will not get into the other position that needs to be avoided:— getting your characters into such a complicated situation that you have to summon the U.S. Cavalry or Superman to rescue them. This sort of last minute, highly unlikely, intervention is called a 'Deus ex machina'. See if you can find out what the words mean and why they are used. . . . . But don't do it!

(a) Here are six essay titles. Write the *endings* for the essays you might have written for each of the titles. All the titles are intended to be for narrative essays. Do not write more than about five or six sentences for each ending. You may use any of the types of ending mentioned in the Factsheet, but in each case clearly note which one yours is.

   (1) *Ever Decreasing Circles.*   (4) *All at Sea.*

   (2) *The Happy Wanderers.*   (5) *A Wish Come True.*

   (3) *Lost in the Forest.*   (6) *A Practical Joke.*   (30)

(b) This time you are given five titles, or instructions, and once again you have to write the endings; but you are also told what sort of ending it has to be.

   (1) *Imagine you are a chess piece. Write a story about your life and adventures.*
   Write an ending that could be described as 'ending with a bang'.

   (2) *Write a composition beginning with the words: "Suddenly I found myself growing. . . . . ."*
   Write an ending that could be described as a 'summing up'.

   (3) *Enemies.*
   Write a 'dying fall' ending for this title.

   (4) *And that taught us never to write on walls.*
   Give this story a 'surprise' ending.

   (5) *You and a friend, or some friends, are on holiday near an old, and partly ruined house. You decide to explore it. Write a story about your adventures in the house.*
   End this story with a piece of speech or dialogue. (Your ending will also qualify under one of the other categories of ending this time — depending on exactly what interesting or entertaining things you have your characters say.)   (20)

(c) Here are some essay titles with the endings that were written for them by pupils aged between eleven and fourteen. In each case the endings are not particularly good — or could at least be distinctly improved. You have two jobs:—

   (i) Explain why these endings are not as good as they might be. (You can criticize any aspect of them which could be improved!) Also try to explain what the writer is attempting to do — and where he or she has gone wrong.   (20)

   (ii) Rewrite the endings so that they are better. You do not have to stick to the ideas in the versions you have been given. You should certainly try to use all the things you have learnt about good writing — not just the information on the facing page. To make a good job of this exercise you will need to think carefully about what you would have written in the rest of the composition.   (20)

   (1) *A Narrow Escape. — A story told by a mouse.*
   I was very pleased that I had not been caught by that huge and horrible cat. So I sat in my hole and ate up all the cheese. It was very nice.

   (2) *The Man Who Never Came.*
   We had had a very good time, even though the person we had been waiting for all day did not arrive. We were both still very glad that we had been waiting for him. So then we went home and had tea.

   (3) *Fire on the Hilltop.*
   We were all dancing up and down around the bonfire and shouting at the top of our voices. Then I saw some people running up the hill, so I shouted out,
   "Hey, you lot, they're coming!"
   Then we all ran off as fast as we could, and they didn't catch any of us, and never found out who we were.

   (4) *Some Day I Will Return.*
   So that was the end of my adventure in Tibet, and everything had turned out quite well. I got a plane back to India, and as I looked out of the window when we took off I thought to myself, "Some day I will return."
   (You need to think carefully about what is wrong here, as the ending looks like a neat 'full circle' coming back to the title. You might ask yourself, though, what the rest of the essay was about, — and whether it had anything to do with the title.)

   (5) *A Day That Changed My Life*
   It had been the most exciting day I had ever had. I enjoyed every moment of it, but now it was over I was tired out. I was glad to get to bed after such a busy day.

FACTSHEET NINETEEN

CHARACTERIZATION

Part of the description which is necessary to any good narrative is a description of the people or *characters* in the story. The characters need to be brought to life as much as or more than the scene. They have to seem like real people, who think and behave like people in 'real life'. Look at this passage:—

"Jo hurried down the stairs as quickly as possible, and had a rushed breakfast. It was already half past nine and the appointment was for ten o'clock.

'Don't bolt your food, dear,' said Mum. Jo groaned, and answered:

'I'm in a hurry, mum. You can't have forgotten! It's my appointment today. — Oh no, I'm going to be late!' "

This is in fact the opening of an essay entitled *The New Job*, and as an opening it is not at all bad. Pause and think for a moment though. What do we know about 'Jo'? For example, had you realised Jo is a girl? And what does she look like? How old is she? What is she wearing? Even a *physical* description of your characters helps; it enables the reader to picture them, and that is always a good thing.

Better still is to give the reader an idea of what the characters think and feel, and in particular how they respond to the things which happen to them in your story. Your aim in fact is to make the events happen because of the sort of people your characters are. This is hard to do in the short space of an essay, but not impossible.

Before we get on to it, however, look back at the example above. It is not true that we have *no* idea of what sort of person Jo is. The words that have been put into her mouth tell us something about her, at least at that particular moment. She is anxious, flustered and a bit disorganized.

If you make your characters speak, you will make them more real. But make sure that the things they say are in fact worth saying. There is a disadvantage to direct speech, with its quotation marks, and new paragraphs: it slows the story down, and if it goes on too long can make the reader lose the thread of the action. Use indirect speech for less important conversation. (For example, *Sue agreed* is quicker than *"I agree," said Sue.*)

In addition to dialogue you can let your readers know what sort of people your characters are by *telling* them. This works quite well with physical descriptions, but is more difficult when you want to explain how someone thought or felt. You can use sentences of this sort:—

"Paul was worried and unhappy. He did not trust Michael and wanted nothing to do with his scheme."

You can also indicate feelings and emotions more subtly by using adverbs and adjectives, and by picking the right synonym.

"Paul's brow furrowed in anxiety, and he glanced suspiciously at Michael" gives the same sort of idea as the earlier version, but doesn't make the statement. it leaves the reader to work it out. Look at these examples:—

" 'I won't do it,' he snarled angrily, staring at Michael with unconcealed distaste."

" 'I don't want to do it,' he sighed wearily, but already there was resignation in his voice."

The speaker's feelings are made very clear by the adverbs used, and the verbs they modify. *Snarled* and *sighed* themselves give very different ideas, and the adverbs help to emphasize them. The second half of each sentence flows naturally from the words used in the first. It is all about using the right words, and fitting the words to the sense you require, in characterization as in all description.

Let's see how things work out in a rather longer passage:—

" 'I'm sure we should take the hill path,' said Douglas, almost jumping up and down with all his new-found confidence. 'The map shows it's only half the distance. — Come on, David!'

David looked at the map again and then up at the hills. He frowned, and glanced at the others for assistance. There were already wisps of mist spreading across the heather and gorse of the long slopes. He knew what he should say, but Douglas was insistent, telling the others they would soon be home by his route.

'Alright, — I suppose so,' David told them, grudgingly. 'But we'll have to hurry.'

They began to climb, and already he knew he was wrong."

See how much we already know about David — the leader of the group, but unable to make up his mind, unwilling to force his choice on 'the others', and too easily persuaded; and Douglas — eager and persuasive. From the sort of people these two *are* comes the decision to take a particular course of action from which the whole story will flow.

The most important thing to notice in this passage is that the story is made to flow from the characters. They are not swept along by the events that the writer has decided on; they make things happen. This is what you want your characters to do. And this is also the way to go about it, by mixing characterization with other pieces of description and action, so that the reader's interest is held, and the story develops naturally — just as things do in 'real life'.

(a) You are given a list of adjectives applying to two very different people. Put the two into a short story together (a couple of paragraphs, say, or about a page of writing). Do it in such a way that you show their different characters. You will need to choose the most suitable background or setting to reveal their personalities.

Person number one:— strong, aggressive, assertive, forceful, arrogant, confident, opinionated, efficient, ambitious.

Person number two:— weak, mild, quiet, diffident, vague, irresolute, hesitant, resigned, conciliatory.

(It would be sensible to check the meanings of any of these words you are unsure of first.)

(20)

(b) This exercise is exactly the same. Once again you have to write a short piece to illustrate the two characters you are given. They can be any people you choose; you might well, for example, want to make number one an adult and number two a boy or girl; on the other hand, if you are particularly clever, you might want to do the exact opposite!

Person number one:— serious, sensible, dutiful, careful, diligent, meticulous, sombre, restrained.

Person number two:— cheerful, happy-go-lucky, playful, heedless, carefree, impulsive, irresponsible.

(20)

(c) Read this passage carefully. Then write down a list of simple adjectives you could apply to each of the two characters in it on the basis of what you learn about them.

"Tara looked doubtfully across at Elsie. Elsie was nearly a year older than her, and infinitely more worldly-wise. She was a better dresser, more fashionable, and more popular. Now the older girl sighed audibly, looked at her fingernails, then began to drum her fingers on the desk.

'It's entirely up to you, dear,' she said in a bored voice. 'Do take your time; I'm sure I've nothing better to do.'

Tara heard the sarcasm in her words, and read the contempt in her eyes. She wanted to snap back a clever reply, but she couldn't find the words. She had never been able to stand up to Elsie. She lowered her eyes, wilting under the sneer."

(20)

(d) The following passage does not have a great deal of characterization in it. Rewrite it, giving the two people some real personality. You can add as much as you like, but you must include all the information from the original:—

"Mr and Mrs Johnstone were having an argument. They were very annoyed with each other. Christine wanted to go on holiday. Her husband, Derek, said they could not afford it that year, and they had to be careful. Christine wouldn't agree with him, but Derek said there was no choice in the matter, and went off to work. His wife went to the travel agent."

(10)

(e) Re-read the 'David and Douglas' story on the Factsheet. Though there is characterization there is no *physical* description of the two. Invent you own descriptions of them. Here are some of the things you should be thinking about:— height, weight, build; age; colour of eyes and hair; distinguishing marks; mannerisms and habits; and clothes.

You have two tasks:—

(1) Make a list of adjectives (or brief adjective phrases) for the physical appearance of each.

(10)

(2) Try to write a descriptive paragraph in which you describe the appearance of each character. Put them both in the same paragraph. You may want to compare and contrast them.

(20)

See if you can make the adjectives you choose and your descriptive paragraph fit in with the sort of people that David and Douglas appear to be in the story on the Factsheet.

FACTSHEET TWENTY

DESCRIPTIVE ESSAYS (1)

You will very often encounter essay titles that require a purely descriptive piece of writing. There is no scope for you to write a narrative or story. These essays are harder to write than narratives because you do not have a framework of events to hang your description on. Worse still, there is no obvious beginning and ending. Look at these titles for descriptive essays:—

The Chimney Sweep.   *Passers-by.*
Aunts and Uncles.   *My Best Friend.*
Teachers I Have Known.   *The Funniest Person I Have Ever Met.*
Imagine you are sitting in a bus or train. Describe your fellow passengers.

You should have noticed that these titles all ask you to describe *people*. This is good news, since you already know a good deal about how to do characterization, and what these titles want is, in effect, one or more character sketches. (Other titles, *Old Age* for example, can also lead into an essay based on character sketches; as always though, make sure you stick to the title and do not twist it round to fit in with what you feel like writing.)

But how do we go about describing people when there is no action to assist? Glance back at the Worksheet you have just done. In (e) you are told what to be thinking about:—

Height, weight, build; age; colour of eyes and hair; distinguishing marks; mannerisms and habits; clothes.

To these we can add another:— facial appearance and expression. A person's face tells you most about him or her, so it is worth its own paragraph. For that is what these categories can easily be — the headings for the paragraphs that will make up your essay. Now, you can see we are getting somewhere. With the paragraph headings we now have the missing framework for the story.

So are there other paragraph headings we can add? So far we have only a physical description, and that is the least part of what makes up a person. We would want paragraphs about a person's job and life-style; behaviour; emotions and moods; relationships with other people; likes and dislikes; thoughts and opinions.

Now of course we have too many headings, but some will be easily combined in the same paragraph, and some will be more important than others. For example, if you were writing the *The Funniest Person I Have Met* essay mentioned above, you would concentrate on what made that person funny:— aspects of his clothes and appearance; his mannerisms and habits; the way he said things — and of course what he said.

You already know how useful speech is to develop characters, — but it is rather more difficult to get it into purely descriptives writing. You can invent situations, though, which have your character doing and saying things — with the assistance of the word *would*:—

"Every morning, without fail, she *would* take the Peke out for a walk. You *could* hear her calling, 'Come along Chu-Chu!' She *used to* dress up in her best clothes, fashionable half century ago, but still beautifully cared for — though I doubt that any moth would dare to nest in her feather boa."

You do not have to employ the 'she would' or 'he used to' technique though. You can put in straightforward pieces of information about what the character does or did:—

"He still smokes that awful pipe now. He buys his 'baccy at the same newsagent, and stands talking to old Mavis behind the counter, just as he has done for ten years or more".

In the example before, about the old lady, there was another 'trick of the trade':— the appearance of 'I'. As with narratives there is a lot to be said for putting yourself into the story. Some character sketches can even be written as conversations between yourself as the 'narrator' and the person you are describing. Without going that far, it is useful to record *your* impressions of and reactions to your characters. Try to give your *reasons* for your reactions to your characters and your feelings about them.

Four of the seven titles mentioned above ask for descriptions of more than one character. Here you obviously cannot be so detailed about each person. On the other hand you have a convenient framework of paragraphs, as you move from person to person. Try to link your paragraphs by linking characters and making them react to each other (rather than to you as the narrator). Look at this example from the last of the titles mentioned above:—

"As the man in the overcoat lit up, I heard the woman next to me sniff, and mutter, 'Well really. This is a non-smoker'. I glanced towards her. . . ."

When it comes to *starting* a descriptive essay about a person or group of people, try to choose a striking and unusual descriptive phrase as your first sentence. Remember that is what you need to catch your reader's attention.

It is quite difficult to end descriptive essays 'with a bang'. They often end with a 'summing up' in fact, though if you use this sort of ending it helps if you can think of an original and interesting last sentence, particularly of the sort that brings the composition 'full circle' back to the title. The 'dying fall' ending also works well for this sort of essay.

(a) Read through this paragraph, which is the opening paragraph from an essay entitled *The Boss* (this time written by a seventeen year-old). Then go onto the three questions.

> "He was a cold, proud and disdainful man. He never addressed his subordinates save with commands. He stared down upon them through gold-rimmed pince-nez, while dabbing his nose with a small handkerchief as if there were an unpleasant odour present. He preferred if possible to communicate with the lower orders by means of an intermediary. He thought nothing of dismissing any man or woman who failed him in the least respect. The plight of these lesser breeds, their hopes, fears, aspirations and dreams were nothing to him. His workers existed solely to serve his requirements, and even then he would have preferred the service of soulless, voiceless robots."

(1) Make a list of adjectives which can be applied to 'the boss' as he is portrayed in this passage. You are not only looking for adjectives actually used by the writer, but also for those which you can infer or deduce from other things said.

(10)

(2) Try to write the second paragraph in this essay, to follow the paragraph you have just read. Obviously what you say must fit in with what has gone before, so you already have a basis for the character of 'the boss'. What you need to do is to go on to describe other aspects of this (unpleasant) character. You might, for example talk about other people's reaction to him; you might want to go back over his life history, to try and explain why he is so unpleasant; you might want to look at the way he behaves at home towards his wife and children. There are plenty of other ways you can continue. Try to link your paragraph to the one that has gone before, and try to make it clear what the 'theme' of your paragraph is in the first sentence. (In the passage above, the author started with three adjectives, and then proceeded to give her reasons for using them in a fuller description.)

(20)

(3) Now try to write a totally different opening paragraph under the same title to suggest a person who is the exact opposite of the one in the passage above. — One way of starting the reversal might be to make the central character a woman rather than a man. You also have the list of adjectives you made for question one to assist you; it might be a good idea to start by jotting down another list of opposite adjectives.

(20)

(b) Write an *essay plan* for each of the following titles. Check Factsheet Sixteen on how to do plans. (It might help to look at the Factsheets on endings and beginnings as well.) Remember you need to divide up your essay under different sorts of headings for each section or paragraph; you cannot do it by sequence of events.

(1) *My Boyfriend* or *My Girlfriend.*
(2) *The Person Who Has Influenced Me Most.* (Think carefully about this one; you are not only writing about the person; you have to talk about yourself as well.)
(3) *Myself When Young.* (Describe what you were like as a small child; you may decide which age to pick — or you may survey yourself at several ages, as you grew older.)
(4) *People Who Live in My Street.*

(20)

(c) For this title: *The Girl (or Boy) with the Bobble-Hat*, write TWO essay plans:—

(1) A plan for a *descriptive* essay.
(2) A plan for a *narrative* essay.

(10)

FACTSHEET TWENTY-ONE

DESCRIPTIVE ESSAYS (2)

We have looked at descriptive essays which centre on describing people. You will often also be asked to describe a scene, as in the following titles:—

Shop Windows   *My Favourite Possessions*
Autumn Leaves   *The Docks*
On the Beach   *Pictures in the Fire*
My Home Town — Write a description of the town, district or village where you live.

Once again you have the problem that there is no framework of events on which to hang your description. So you need alternative frameworks. Here are some possibilities:—

THE SENSES:— Remember you have more senses than sight. With some subjects you can divide your essay into sections based on the five senses. So for the title *The Old Oak Tree,* when you have described its appearance you can go on to talk about the feel of its bark, the sound of the wind in its branches, even the smell of its piles of fallen leaves in autumn. (If it had been a chestnut tree, you could even have included taste!) Though this method will often provide you with part of an essay's structure, it will not usually make up the whole composition. You will need to combine it with some of the other methods which follow.

A HISTORY:— This involves looking back at what you are describing across the years, or else following it through the cycle of seasons. With titles like *Village Fields* or *Woodland Creatures* to divide your essay up with a paragraph or two devoted to each season is quite a good way of setting it out. You can imagine yourself watching the subject through the turning year. Alternatively, with a title like *The Old Church* you could look back over its history through the years as well as, or instead of, watching it through one year. Every scene will have its history, and even if you do not build your whole composition round it, it can still make a good paragraph or two within the essay.

A SURVEY:— When you have to describe a scene it is very often possible simply to rotate in a complete circle, describing what you see in each direction, — or to imagine an aerial view and work across it in one direction, taking things item by item. If you do this, try to pick out the most important things to describe, and make these the centre of each paragraph. Try to give a broad general picture, and then bring it to life with precise pieces of detail. Do not try to describe every detail of everything. Include what is interesting, and what will help the reader picture the scene; leave out what is boring.

As the last approach was historical, we could call this one geographical! The two can very often be combined to make an effective essay. Incidentally it is very easy to *link* your paragraphs by the position of things:— "Just down the High Street from the cinema is the Town Market." — You can also put yourself into a scene, and stroll about describing what you see as you come to it.

ASPECTS:— By this method you pick out a few things you consider important about what you are describing, and concentrate on them. This approach is often useful when you do not have a particular *place* to describe, as in the *My Favourite Possessions* title. Sometimes essay instructions tell you to concentrate on particular aspects.

IMAGINATION:— Some descriptive essay titles are really asking you to imagine things. The title *Pictures in the Fire* is a good example. You might start by imagining the flames as dancing figures, then as faces; then you might see the sparks as a forest of vivid trees, and then as lost souls blown away forever. Each scene is its own paragraph.

A good descriptive essay will often include elements of all these different techniques. It will need careful planning, though, to fit them together into a single account.

There is another sort of essay title you often come across, which invites you to combine narration and description. For example:—

My Family   *My birthday*   *An Outing in the Park*
A Visit to the Fairground   *A School Day*   *What I Did on My Holidays.*

Writing about your holidays always seems terribly boring, and is perhaps best avoided if you have the choice. In exams, however, you can be 'economical with the truth' (which means 'tell lies' — see Factsheet Three) so long as you do not go over the top. Do not have your flight to Ibiza hi-jacked to Beirut — unless of course it was; but do have a spot of aerial turbulence which caused your younger brother to be sick — and not in the bag provided.

In fact this sort of essay should not present too many difficulties. You can use the framework of events happening one after the other, as in any narrative, to form the basis of your story and the structure of your essay plan, but can also use some of the alternative techniques mentioned on this page for some of the paragraphs. As always, remember to vary action with description. Even in purely descriptive essays there is a great deal of action happening around you!

(a) Here is the opening paragraph from a descriptive essay entitled *Autumn Days*. Read through it carefully then answer the questions which follow.

"Leaves fall. Clouds hurry in the sky. The colours change, green to gold to red to dying. Children's kites shiver in the singing wind and rush and dip. Their owners shout and laugh, run to keep warm, kick the piled leaves into rustling swirls and flurries. And blue turns to dove-grey up above. There birds wheel, black specks in the wind, congregate in skyward whirlpools, trickle away in flights to the southward, abandon the rough-barked bare trees. The last of the leaf-robes now are tattered rags. The smell of the smoke of their burning fills the air."

(1) Copy out this paragraph, and underline all the verbs in it which are straightforward actions — the words for things which are *done*.

Also say how many times the verb *to be* is used, as this is a good indication of how many pieces of 'pure' description there are.

(10)

(Also, to improve your own writing, notice how all these action words are used to build up the descriptive picture and create a particular impression.)

(2) Explain how the writer of the passage uses the senses of sight, smell, touch and hearing.

(10)

(3) Devise an essay plan for the rest of this essay, following on from the first paragraph you have been given. (For this question, and for (b) and (c) below, you might want to check back to Factsheet Sixteen again.)

(10)

(4) Write the second paragraph of the essay — the one which would follow the paragraph you already have — according to your essay plan. Try to write it in the same way as the one you were given. (The first thing you need to remember here is that the first paragraph is entirely in the present tense.)

(10)

(b) Here are four essay titles. Write essay plans for descriptive essays for each of them. In each case the method you should use in constructing your framework is specified.
(1) *Pictures in the Fire* (Imaginative)
(2) *The Old Church* (Historical)
(3) *My Home Town* (A Survey)
(4) *The Seashore* (The Senses)

(20)

(c) Write essay plans for these four titles. You can use any of the methods for descriptive essays, or a narrative framework, or a combination of both.
(1) *A Day at the Beach*   (3) *He was certainly a curious fellow* . . .
(2) *Christmas Presents*   (4) *Ill in Bed*

(20)

(d) Here is a very brief essay plan — just the paragraph framework. The title is *The Docks*. Your task is to write the essay based on the plan.
Para. 1 An aerial view — survey and broad sweep.
Para. 2 The warehouses, dockside, cargo and cranes.
Para. 3 The passenger terminals, and the people waiting to board ferries or cruise ships.
Para. 4 The ships themselves — large and small, passenger or freighters.
Para. 5 History: thinking back to other ships that once docked here.
Para. 6 Imaginative: thinking about the other countries to which the ships sail; bringing the story back to the docks with the returning cargoes and people.
Para. 7 Ending with a summary, picking out some of the more striking aspects of the scene.

(30)

FACTSHEET TWENTY-TWO

EXPLANATION AND ARGUMENT

Some of the essay titles we have already considered, like *My Holiday; A Railway Journey; My Relations*, are 'factual' (apart from the little extras you have made up!); so are many descriptive essays with titles like *The Old Church* and *The Market Place*. But in all of them, in addition to explaining the facts pure and simple, we have another element — imaginative description, or a narrative story. Some factual essays are much more mechanical; they give you less scope for imaginative and original writing. What they want is a straightforward EXPLANATION of something. These titles are examples of this sort of essay:—

Model-Making as a Hobby	*The Red Cross Organization*	*How to Drive a Car*
Ballet	*The Rules of Football*	*Horse Riding*

Because you have less run for your imagination, essays of this type are harder to do. In an examination, where you have a choice, unless there is a topic about which you do in fact know a great deal, it is best not to do an 'explanation' essay. Since it is essential to know what you are talking about if you write an 'explanation' essay, look up the subject first in a good reference book. (This can be difficult in an exam!) Your essay will still contain a great deal of description, but the aim this time is not to be original and striking; it is to be precise and accurate. Your description will be varied with explanation, — explaining how the thing you have just described *works* — whether it is a particular rule in soccer, a transistor in a radio, or an ambulance.

When planning an essay of this sort it is sensible to start with a definition:— say exactly what it *is* that you are writing about. The natural ending is simply a summary. The structure of the plan may follow a series of steps in progression if you are giving instructions (as in *How to Drive a Car*), or the different stages in a process (as for *Model-Making*), or the different parts or sections of something starting with the most important (as for *The Rules of Football*, or for any title asking you to explain or describe a piece of equipment). One final useful tip — try to be as clear and straightforward as you can; you may well have to simplify for readers who know even less about the topic than you do!

The other category of essays we are looking at on this Factsheet comes under the headings ARGUMENT or DISCUSSION. They are very often introduced by the word *Discuss* (or sometimes by *compare* or *contrast* two different views or opinions). They are often also simply put as questions. Here are some typical titles of this kind:—

Discuss the Advantages of Learning a Foreign Language	*Spooks are Spoofs. — Discuss.*
Cruel sports should be banned. Do you agree?	*Should there be school uniforms?*
Are private schools better than state schools?	*The Death Penalty: Right or Wrong?*

There are in fact many other titles which also invite a discussion or argument, but it is less obvious when you first look at them. Here are some other examples:—

Women in Politics	*Nuclear Disarmament*	*The Loch Ness Monster*	*Prison Reform*
The Advantages and Disadvantages of Boarding Schools		*My Kind of Music*	*How to be Happy*

Clearly there is an element of *explanation* in these titles, but what they are really looking for is a *discussion*, a statement of *opinions*. We have to start with a word of warning. Most people marking essays in exams are not really interested in your opinions at all (hard though that may be to believe). They want to see if you can argue a case, give reasons for what you think, give both sides of the argument — and do it in good English. So do not rush into a title of this sort on the basis of "Oh, good, I hate school uniform, so I'll do that essay . . ." The chances are that you will put your reader off by frequent statements of "in my opinion", especially if they are not supported by careful and reasoned argument.

So how do we go about it? — Firstly decide what the two sides of the argument are. Make a list of the main points on *each* side. Even if you are told to argue one side only; you still need to knock down the opposition, so you need to know what you are attacking. — Assuming you aren't told which side to support, pick the one you do favour. It is possible to end without making up your mind, but it is not very satisfactory in an essay. Better to jump one way or the other. Your set of paired arguments, for and against, are your essay plan. (You will need to think of more than one argument for and against of course!) Remember each point on each side must be supported by its reasons. You are trying to persuade your reader, not bully him into a particular point of view.

A good way of starting this essay, as for the *explanation* type, is with a *definition*. State clearly and precisely exactly what the title means (and possibly what it does not mean). You might also briefly mention in the first paragraph something of the history of the argument (as in the case of the long political debate about the death penalty for example).

For ending your essay, you should summarise the most important arguments, mention the objections to them in passing, and then explain why you have come to the conclusion you have. This is the sort of essay that really does have a *conclusion:* you have carefully weighed the arguments and you end by making your choice (and saying why!)

(a) Your first task is to write an essay plan for a composition of the *explanation* type. The title is:— *Describe the nature of the work done by a person in any one job, trade or profession of your choice.*

Before you start of course you must decide which job you want to write about. Pick one you know something about: perhaps what your mother or father does, or the profession you want to follow yourself. There are various ways you could do the plan. The simplest method is probably to give a paragraph to each of the tasks a person would have to perform, or each of the skills he or she would need to employ. You might put in a paragraph (possibly even as your introduction) to describe a typical day for a person in that trade, — though you should not try to build your whole essay round this idea. Alternatively you could start by giving a brief preview of what the job involves. You could finish by giving your opinion of the job; what makes it interesting or boring, hard or easy, good or bad. But do make sure you give the reasons for any opinions you express.   (20)

(b) Probably the best way to teach you how to write a *discussion* essay is to make you do one! You do have a great deal of help, however, since a detailed essay plan is provided for you. You may add to it if you wish, but keep to the general framework it provides. If you want to look up additional information to provide more detail for your essay, by all means do so.   (30)

The title is: *Spooks are Spoofs: Discuss*

Para. 1   Definition: say what the title means.
Spooks means ghosts (of any sort).
(So mention that there are many types: ghosts in haunted houses/churchyards; spirits at seances; poltergeists etc.)
Spoofs means hoaxes or practical jokes.
So the title isn't the same as the statement: 'Ghosts do not exist'. It says they are *deliberate fakes*.

Para 2.   Historical survey: Mankind has always believed in spirits; primitive peoples; Ancient Egypt and the mummies; ghosts, witches and demons in the Middle Ages.
The decline of these beliefs when scientific explanation arrived.

Paras. 3 and 4.   Seances and spiritualism: FOR   AGAINST

Remarkable cases of spirit appearances	Appearances and photographs are easy to fake
Some of them photographed	Many fakes have been exposed, and the frauds have admitted it.
Some seen by eminent people	Many people want to believe and so convince themselves
Spirits/mediums having super-natural knowledge.	Stage magicians can do the same tricks.

Paras. 5 and 6.   Hauntings: FOR   AGAINST

There have been an enormous number recorded over the years	It is in the interests of people to fake hauntings: from tourism to smuggling (as in *Moonfleet!*)
They have been reported by people who did not know of them in advance	No photo is convincing; all are unlikely; some are obvious fakes
There have been photos.	Perhaps people only *think* they are seeing ghosts; tricks of the light or wishful thinking.
The number of observers is too great to explain away.	

Paras. 7 and 8.   Poltergeists: FOR   AGAINST

The large number of cases	There is also proof of trickery in some of the cases,
They are all of the same type	and some of the evidence has been proved to be
The physical evidence is so great and some of it could not possibly have been faked.	faked.

Para. 9 Conclusion: There is a great deal of evidence. Some is faked. Some more can be explained by other causes. Some cannot be explained.
Clearly not all spooks are spoofs — tricks or frauds — some are; it is less clear what the unexplained cases might be.

(c) There is just one more task. Now you have seen an essay plan in full, write your own essay plans, set out in the same sort of way, for these two *discussion* essays:—

(1) *Was it a mistake to abolish corporal punishment in schools?*

(2) *Democracy is a bad form of government; but all the other forms are much worse. Discuss.*   (20)

FACTSHEET TWENTY-THREE

LETTERS

Letters fall into two main categories: business or official letters, and personal letters. Everyone should know how to set out a letter, — and they are sometimes set instead of essays as an exercise; so it is worth going through the general rules, at least for the layout of the letter.

(1) Write your own address, or the address from which you are writing, at the top right hand side of the page (unless you have headed notepaper with the address already on; if you are working for a business, and are writing on their behalf, this will often be the case).

Give each part of the address its own line in this order:— *House name* (if any) first; then give the *number* of the house or flat and the *street name*; then the *district* (in a town); *or* the *village* name (in the country) — if any; then the *town* (or nearest town); the *county*; and finally the *postcode* if you happen to know it.

At the end of each line of the address (except the last) you may, if you wish, put a comma.

At the end of the address, miss a line, and then write the *date*.

(2) When you are replying to a business or official letter they often have a code of letters and numbers somewhere at the top right. This is called a *reference*. Include it in your reply, somewhere under the date. (For example:— *Ref: CF/112.*)

(3) If you are writing an official or business letter, write the name of the person (or organization) you are writing to, and set out the address in the same way, a little lower down than your own, and on the *left* hand side. There is no need at all to do so on a personal letter.

(4) On the left hand side begin your letter *Dear Sir* or *Dear Madam*, if you do not know the name of the person to whom you are writing; it is better if you can find out the person's name, and write *Dear Mr Smith*, or *Dear Miss Jones*. If you are not sure whether it is a man or woman you are writing to, or if it is some nameless person in a large organization, put *Dear Sir*. Notice the capital letters. After the *Dear Sir* (or *Dear Jack* or *Dear Jill*) part, put a comma, and then continue the letter itself after the comma — *on the next line*.

(5) If you are writing a business or official letter, it is often a good idea to write a title on the first line of the proper letter — to tell the reader what it is about — and since it is a title it should be underlined.

(6) At the end of your letter, if you began *Dear Sir* or *Dear Madam* (i.e. if you do not know a person's name), it is correct to end with the words: *Yours faithfully*. Put them on a new line, in from the edge like a new paragraph, follow them with a comma, and notice that *Yours* has a capital letter, and *faithfully* does not. Then you sign your name on the next line.

If the person you are writing to does not know who you are, *print* your name clearly under the signature. (You know no-one can read your writing!)

If you are writing an official or business letter to someone whose name you do know (so you will have begun *Dear Mrs Black* etc.) it is normal to end *Yours sincerely*. You can also use this for personal letters to people you are not particularly close to. To closer friends and close members of your family you can use many different informal endings: *Yours, Yours as ever, 'Bye for now, All the best, Love*, etc.— or a combination of two of these.

Well, that is how to set it out; now what should you say in it? There are a few guidelines it is sensible to follow when you write a letter.

If your letter is at all complicated or very long, it is well worth treating it like any other essay, and writing a *plan* first. This may be just a few paragraph headings, to remind you what you want to say. (Do write letters in paragraphs, like any essay — for the sake of your reader.) If it is an important letter, do a more detailed plan, and if you are still uncertain, do a rough draft first.

Any business letter or official letter needs to be accurate and carefully set out. If you are asking for something, make it plain what it is; if you are describing something, do so precisely. Do not leave any room for doubt in the reader's mind about what you want or what you are saying. In these respects a letter of this sort is like a factual essay. In a letter, unlike an essay, you can state important facts in a numbered list, and for the sake of clarity it may well be worth doing so.

You need to get the *tone* of your letter right. This is part of the idea of giving a particular impression. In a personal letter, you need a chatty, conversational tone, giving the news and your comments on it. You will not need long words and formal language very much in this sort of letter. In the official or business letter, you need to be more careful of the language you use. Unfortunately, officials seem to take more notice of official language. They like to write "I am in receipt of your communication of the 11th inst." when they mean "I have received your letter of the 11th of this month." You need to use formal language too, in the sense that you have to be precise, accurate, clear and correct. Always be polite in letters, even if you are threatening someone with legal action. On the other hand, do not grovel or 'creep' to officials:— so the rule is *polite but firm*.

(a) Here is a letter written by a young man about a job. In addition to what the letter tells you, you might like to know that it was sent to Mrs Stickler, Personnel Manager of Sharp and Tack Ltd, of 100a, Newstart Industrial Estate, Brightley, Bucks., in response to an advertisement in the *Pall Mall Gazette* for trainee technicians.

> Flat 5d, Slopers Court
> London N4

> Dear manager,
>   I saw your advert in last night's Gazette. Could you let me know a bit more about the jobs you've got going there.
> Thanks very much, Joe Laidback.

  (1)   Criticize the layout and contents of this letter. Mention good points as well as bad.   (20)

  (2)   Now write your own version of the letter, asking for information about the advertised jobs. (Notice you do not actually have to apply for the job). Write it as Mr Joe Laidback, but do not use his style!   (20)

(b) Imagine you are writing to request a refund for a broken vacuum cleaner. Your letter is to the manager of the shop where you bought it. The rough notes for the letter (which will form your plan) are given to you. You can fill in any details that are necessary. Make up any names and addresses that are involved. Start with a heading.

  (1)   Date of buying; receipt enclosed
  (2)   Date first used; amount of use
  (3)   Date broken; make it clear it was in normal usage
  (4)   Describe the breakage
  (5)   Sum up the above briefly, as grounds for refund
  (6)   State what is required: full refund
        and what is not required:— repairs or replacement
  (7)   Ask for reply soon

Remember, when you write your letter, *be polite but firm!*   (20)

(c) Read through this letter from the Inland Revenue Department:—

> Inland Revenue Department
> Fork Street
> Morton
> PA6 7YE.
> 1st April 1988

> Roger Crook Esq.,
> Cayman Mansions,
> 1 Rich Street,
> Bankerton
> Cashshire.

> Your Ref: OD/2/US

> Dear Sir,
> With reference to your outstanding tax returns for the financial year ending 31st March, 1983, I would be most obliged if you would favour me with a reply to my communication of 23rd May, 1986 and subsequent reminders. I am instructed to inform you that failure to comply with the provisions of the Involuntary Extortions Act of 1946 may result in the imposition of unlimited fines and/or a period of imprisonment.
> Yours faithfully,
>   I. Nickit,
>   H.M. Inspector of Taxes.

Imagine you are the disreputable Mr Crook, and reply to this letter, making your excuses for not sending the form they require. (Perhaps you were ill.) Promise to let them have what they want in the course of the next year or so . . . Try not to admit you are in the wrong!   (20)

(d) Here are some sentences taken from official or business letters. Re-write them in plain English so that we can begin to understand what they mean:—

  (1)   With reference to your communication of 23rd inst., we beg to inform you that your inquiry is receiving our active consideration.

  (2)   We are in receipt of your esteemed order, and would be most obliged if you would settle outstanding invoices on your account to facilitate early delivery of items requested.

  (3)   All necessary particulars not having been received to date, it would be inexpedient to institute further inquiries at this moment in time.

  (4)   Having regard to the changed circumstances of the case, it is envisaged that every step will be taken to expedite the implementation of the initial directive.   (20)

FACTSHEET TWENTY-FOUR

SUMMARIES AND REVIEWS

The purpose of a summary is to give the reader the main points of a passage, while leaving out everything that is not essential to understanding it. Summaries are very useful: they give you the facts briefly, without your having to wade through a great deal of description and explanation which may be useful but is not vital.

When you have to do a summary, therefore, the main question to bear in mind is:—

What is essential, and what can we manage without?

All the points about interesting the reader, entertaining him, setting the scene, creating an impression, and so on, do not apply in a summary. You want none of these things. You just want the simple facts, explained as clearly, precisely, and *shortly* as possible.

There used to be a 'rule' that a summary should be one third the length of the original, and you may find it helpful to aim for this. In fact, however, the summary should be as long as it takes to say what is necessary. Sometimes a very long-winded piece can be summed up in a couple of sentences!

If the passage you are summarizing is well-written, each paragraph should be self-contained, with its own subject matter. So you can go through it paragraph by paragraph taking out the key items. What you are doing, in a way, is working back from the essay to the plan. The topic of each paragraph will give you a series of section headings — the bare essentials that make up the main points of your summary. These may be enough in themselves, but it is more likely that you will need to include some additional explanation. Check that you have not missed out any essential information by reading through the headings and notes you have jotted down. Make sure that everything still hangs together and makes sense.

The remaining task is to write up your notes in good English — which means in proper sentences. Summaries should *not* be written in 'note form', unless the instructions tell you to do so. Do not add any additional information at this stage. Remember that you are trying to keep things short.

Most summaries are of facts and information, not of narrative or descriptive essays. There is an important exception to this though:— the book review (or the review of the play, film, television programme, opera, etc.)

A review combines two skills. Firstly you have to summarize the work you are reviewing. Secondly you have to comment on it; this is the skill you need in writing an essay which asks for your opinions or a discussion.

Summarizing a whole book is harder than summarizing a short passage or an essay, because there is simply so much in a book. You can follow the same general principle and try to sum up each chapter in a sentence or two, and having the book open at the contents page will often help to jog your memory at this stage. (It is harder still if you are in an exam and do not have the book available!)

It is often a good idea to begin a review by saying what sort of story you are writing about. Is it adventure, romance, science fiction, or what? Then, mention the leading characters (as long as there are not too many) round whom the story revolves. Once you have said who the characters are, still in the introduction to your review, try to explain in a sentence or two what the *plot* of the story is. The plot is a very abbreviated outline of events, — so what you are doing here is a summary of your summary! For example, you might write:—

"The two heroes are both seeking an ancient treasure. The book describes their search. One of them is killed in the attempt. The other realises that there are other things more important and abandons the search."

This stage in the process is in fact important. Book reviews written by people of your age very often fail to give a clear idea (or even *any* idea) of the *story*.

Try to mix your opinions with the writing of the summary. If your second paragraph describes the events of the first four chapters of the book, and you thought they were very slow and boring, and much too complicated, then say so. Apart from anything else, it will serve to explain to your reader why your summary is also rather complicated!

As well as the chapter-by-chapter approach it is worth giving the characters of the story a paragraph. You know now how to do characterization. Apply what you have learnt to the book you are discussing. Did the author make a good job of the characterization? Similarly, as you present your opinions, you should always be asking yourself questions like:—

"Is the description good?" "Is the narrative clear?" "Can I visualize this scene?"

The 'review' essay usually ends with a summing up of your opinions — stating clearly why and in what ways you thought it was a good or bad book.

There is one other sort of 'reverse summary' that should be mentioned. That is when you have to describe or explain in words a plan, map, or diagram. The purpose of getting you to do this is to make you prove you can understand, plans, diagrams etc. (which are themselves very convenient forms of summary). So treat this sort of thing as a straightforward 'explanation' essay, and in writing it be precise, accurate and factual.

(a) Write a summary of the story-line or *plot* of the following paragraph. Remember to concentrate on the events, — the things that happened, rather than the description. Also remember that you are trying to include what is necessary to the story, and to leave out what is inessential.

> It was a dull and drizzling day, the worst possible day for such a foolish venture. Best to go back. The girl pushed away the thoughts that raced through her mind. There could be no going back now. She paused under the straggling trees at the foot of the cliff, wiped the rain from her face and pushed her lank hair back from her eyes. She stared long and carefully, screwing up her eyes in concentration, back along the valley. There was no sign of pursuit. There was no sound of the dogs through the hiss and patter of the rain. She looked up through the branches at the rocks above. Then, not giving herself time to think, she hurried through the little copse, and without pausing began to climb. Her feet slipped on the wet stone, slid on the slimy moss and grass. Her hands and legs were soon cut and bleeding from the frequent falls, blood mingling with rain on her skin. Once she slipped back yards and yards down a scree slope. Lying there, bruised and gasping, in that moment she heard again the baying of the hounds.

(20)

(b) Now you have written a summary of the above passage, give your opinion of it. Is it well written? Do you get a clear impression of the scene? Do you learn much about what sort of person the character in the story is? (Of course you do not have the whole of the story in front of you, so you can only say whether this particular paragraph 'works' as a piece of writing. It might help you to know that the girl in the story is a runaway slave.)

(10)

(c) Still on the same passage, now you have given your opinion on the writing, and summarized the events, try to write a brief description of the scene where these occur. (So you are trying to summarize the *descriptive* parts of the story.)

(10)

(d) Here is another passage to summarize. You will probably find it more difficult, because it is complicated and full of details. You have to decide which details are essential, as far as this paragraph is concerned, and which can safely be omitted without losing any of the sense.

> The French were advancing steadily along the defile towards the Crossroads of St. Denis. They had every reason to believe that their march through the Sansespoir Hills had remained undetected. Certainly their outriders had reported no sign of any English presence, either in the pass itself or on the heights above. Maréchal Maladroit had taken the precaution of scouting the Forest of Surêté on his right, but had ignored the Wood of Brouiller that ran along the hills to his left and came down to the crossroads itself on the plain. He had no reason to believe that the English could have crossed the River Belvue to his north and entered the wood. His omission was to prove fatal. The Earl of Itchen had forded the stream on the previous day, and positioned his knights and mounted infantry within the edge of the wood, invisible to the enemy, but able to look out on the scene of the impending battle, and play their part when the time came. Sir Harry FitzMort, meanwhile, was in command of the archers, stationed in three wedge-shaped formations across the crossroads and facing the oncoming French. The English infantry were already moving up from the south to form the third side of the trap into which the French were steadily marching.

(30)

(e) Among all the detailed information in this passage there is a good deal of geographical description. Summarize the lie of the land. This means you have to describe the countryside, saying where woods, hills, the crossroads, the pass or defile, — and possibly the river — were in relation to each other. As a result of your careful summary, it should be possible to draw a map of the scene. (You could prove the point by *trying* to draw a map of the scene!)

(10)

(f) Look back to Worksheet Fifteen. Your task is to write a summary of the passage on that page, *in not more than sixty words*.

(20)

(g) Look back to Worksheet Twenty-Two. You had to write an essay about ghosts entitled *Spooks are Spoofs: Discuss*. Now write a summary of *your* essay (not of the essay plan, but of what you actually wrote). Try to make it no more than a third of the length of your original.

(20)

FACTSHEET TWENTY-FIVE

POETRY (1)

You are sometimes, in exams, given the option, among a choice of essays, of writing a poem instead. You may well be good at writing poetry if you are good at descriptive writing — if you are imaginative, if metaphors spring naturally to your mind. You do need something else, though, and that is a good sense of *rhythm*. If your powers of description are not particularly good or you do not have much sense of rhythm, — stick to prose writing. ('Prose', by the way, means any writing that is not verse.)

The secret to writing verse is to *alternate stressed syllables with unstressed syllables* in a regular pattern. A syllable is a separate sound; so *impossible* has four syllables: *im — poss — ib — le*, while *create* has only two: *cre — ate*. When you stress a syllable you give it a little more emphasis than an unstressed syllable.

Look at these lines of verse, read them aloud, and notice where the stress falls:—

>"Twinkle, twinkle, little bat;
>How I wonder what you're at,
>Up above the world so high,
>Like a tea-tray in the sky."

For each of these four lines, we could take out the words and write:—

>*Dum di dum di dum di dum*

The *dums* are what we stress, and the *dis* are what we do not stress!

You can do this with any line of verse:—

"The curfew tolls the knell of parting day" = Di dum — di dum — di dum — di dum — di dum.
"Arise ye and shine, bright ladies divine" = Di dum — di di dum — di dum — di di dum.

In case you are embarrassed by going round saying 'dum-di-dum', you can call the unstressed syllables *short*, and indicate them in writing by putting a mark that looks like a *cup* over them; and call the stressed ones *long*, and indicate them by a *line*. It is also usual to divide lines of verse up into sections, called, believe it or not, *feet*. A *foot* usually has one stressed syllable and one or more unstressed syllables. This whole curious process of dividing up lines of verse is called scanning or scansion. Here is a piece of poetry with the scansion done:—

>I wan|dered lone|ly as|a cloud
>
>That floats|on high|o'er vale|and hill,
>
>When all|at once|I spied|a crowd,
>
>A host|of gol|den daf|fodils.

This is an example of the simplest rhythm you find in poetry, where each line has four feet, each of a short syllable followed by a long one. It is not always so simple. The next two lines of the same poem (*Daffodils* by William Wordsworth) go:—

>Beneath|the lake,|beneath|the trees,   (The same scansion.)
>
>Fluttering and|dancing in the|breeze.   (Distinctly different.)

In case you want to show off your poetic knowledge the most common feet in English verse have the following names:—
Starting with a *short*:— the *iambus* ∪ — ; and the *anapaest* ∪∪—
Starting with a *long*:— the *trochee* —∪ ; and the *dactyl* —∪∪ .

You do not need to know all the names — just how to use the things they refer to.

So how does this help you to write poetry?

What it does is give you a pattern for the rhythm. It is like the framework of an essay, that you create when you draw up the essay plan. The structure of a poem, or a song, or any piece of music in fact, is one of rhythm. In a poem you are fitting words onto that framework. That is where your creative abilities as a great writer come into the picture. The construction of the framework is a mere mechanical skill. But you cannot begin to write the words, until you know how to build the rhythmical framework. If you have a strong sense of rhythm, you may be able to hold the pattern of it in your head. While you are learning how to do it, there is a great deal to be said for writing it down.

(a) Here are some lines of poetry. Write them out, and above the words put the marks for short or long syllables. Remember that a syllable is a separate sound, as in *de-cide*: two syllables. You do not have to divide the syllables up into poetic feet for this exercise. (That comes later!)

　(1)　Now sleeps the crimson petal, now the white. . . .
　(2)　The sun came up upon the left. . . .
　(3)　Of man's first disobedience and the fruit. . . . (NOTE — *ience* counts as one syllable here.)
　(4)　There came a wind out of the north. . . .
　(5)　Ye learnéd sisters which have oftentimes. . . . (NOTE — the *-ed* of *learnéd* has an accent on it to show
　　　　　　　　　　　　　　　　　　　　that it is pronounced)　　　　　　　　　　　　　　(10)

(b) All the lines in (a) were in fact made up of iambics: ∪— . Check that your versions are also made up of iambics, and now divide the lines up into poetic feet. Set your scansion out in the same way as the example (*Daffodils*) was done on the Factsheet.　　　　　　　　　　　　　　　　　　　　　　　　　　　　(10)

(c) This time you have some 'couplets' (pairs of lines of verse that go together — not to be confused with 'cutlets'). Try to do the complete scansion of them, marking the long and short syllables, and dividing the lines up into feet at the same time. They have various different rhythms, so think carefully, — and try saying the lines aloud, so that you can work out the patterns of alternating stressed and unstressed syllables.

　(1)　Shall I compare thee to a Summer's day?
　　　　Thou art more lovely and more temperate. . .

　(2)　In ancient times, as story tells,
　　　　The saints would often leave their cells. . .

　(3)　Take, O take those lips away,
　　　　That so sweetly were foresworn. . .

　(4)　Every day the starving poor
　　　　Crowded around Bishop Hatto's door. . .

　(5)　Holy, holy, holy, all the saints adore Thee,
　　　　Casting down their golden crowns around the glassy sea. . .　　　　　　　　　(30)

(d) Now it is time to have a go at fitting your own words into a framework. Here is a skeleton of the short and long syllables, and the poetic feet, for one verse of a poem. Next to it set out one real example of how you could put the flesh on it. You may, if you feel like it, try to make alternate lines rhyme in the same way as the example. All you *have* to do is get the rhythm right in your own verse.

Framework:—　　　　　　　　　　　　Example:—

∪—|∪—|∪—|∪—|　　　　　　　　　I looked upon the rotting sea,

∪—|∪—|∪—|　　　　　　　　　　　And drew my eyes away;

∪—|∪—|∪—|∪—|　　　　　　　　　I looked upon the rotting deck,

∪—|∪—|∪—|　　　　　　　　　　　And there the dead men lay.　　　　　　　　　(25)

(e) This is exactly the same principle. Make up your own verse of a poem, on any subject you like to fit the 'skeleton' you are given. The metre is the same as in (f), but the second and fourth lines are 'one foot' longer. (*Metre* means the sort of poetic foot you employ, plus the line length. We could call the sort of metre in this question and (d) iambic. (Why?))

Framework:—　　　　　　　　　　　　Example:—

∪—|∪—|∪—|∪—|　　　　　　　　　Come live with me and be my love,

∪—|∪—|∪—|∪—|　　　　　　　　　And we will all the pleasures prove,

∪—|∪—|∪—|∪—|　　　　　　　　　That hills and valleys, dales and fields

∪—|∪—|∪—|∪—|　　　　　　　　　Or woods or steepy mountain yields.

Once again, you may use rhymes. This time make lines one and two rhyme, and then lines three and four.　　　　(25)

FACTSHEET TWENTY-SIX

POETRY (2)

You now have a fair idea about the mechanics of how to write verse. There are some rules about the *layout* of poetry, which you also need to know.

As you know, each new line of a poem should begin with a capital letter. (Lines do not have to end with a full stop or even a comma, unless you need one there anyway.)

When you have a poem where a longer line is followed by a shorter one, you can if you wish indent the shorter lines, as in this example:—

> She dwelt among the untrodden ways
> Beside the springs of Dove,
> A maid whom there were none to praise
> And very few to love.

Simple verses like the one above, or verses consisting of two pairs of rhyming lines, each with four feet, are probably the most common forms of layout. There are much more complicated forms, with set variations of line length and patterns of rhyme. (One that you may hear mentioned is the Sonnet; another the Ode; but do not worry too much about them at this stage.)

From your point of view, it is best to stick to the simple forms — though you can make the lines longer if you want to, with five or six feet in them. Whatever you are going to do, draw up a plan of the layout of the lines and the metre beforehand, — just as you would plan an essay.

Because it is often difficult to make what you want to say fit in with the metre (or the rhyme), various poetic tricks can be used. You have already seen that an accent can be put on the final -*ed* of a word like *learned* — so that there is an extra syllable available to fit the metre. There are also poetic abbreviations, like *o'er* and *e'er* for *over* and *ever,* and the antique verb forms: *thou lovest, she loveth* etc. If you can manage without this sort of thing, try to do so, — at least until you are a famous poet. (Because *they* all use them!)

Since we have already mentioned *rhyme* several times, that had better be the next topic we discuss. You can make pairs of lines rhyme (but usually only if they are the same length); or you can make every other line rhyme — so in a four line verse only the second and fourth lines would rhyme. Yet another possibility is to rhyme alternate lines, as in the example above. Alternatively, you do not need to make your poetry rhyme at all. If your poetry has rhythm, and you have written it in a good metrical form, it will work pretty well without rhyme. However, it may also work rather better if you can insert rhymes.

Fairly long lines (five or six feet, and known, just to entertain you, as *pentameters* and *hexameters*) work quite well without rhymes. Shorter ones seem to need them rather more. If you are using the layout of the example above, you really do need at least to make the second and fourth lines rhyme. This sort of metre sounds odd without rhyme!

If you are going to use rhyme, and on balance it is a good thing if you can, try not to use obscure words at the end of the line. Do use words that are single syllables, or end with a good solid long syllable. There are a couple of poetic tricks to assist you. Firstly you can re-arrange the order of words:—

> And sometimes through the mirror blue
> The knights come riding two and two . . .

Here in ordinary language we would say 'blue mirror', but for the sake of the rhyme, the word are reversed. Only do this as long as it is still obvious what you mean, and avoid it altogether if you can. It is better than using 'near rhymes' though:—

> Not Caesar's empress would I deign to prove;
> No, make me mistress to the man I love.

Prove and *love* are 'near rhymes' — but as you can see, the device does not really work very well. (In this particular example, the poet has also had to use a complicated phrase 'deign to prove' when he meant 'be' even to get to a bad rhyme!)

If you really cannot cope with rhyme, but do want to write poetry, stick to longer lines and write 'blank verse' (verse with no rhyme). After all most of Shakespeare's verse is blank verse. Before we leave the topic of rhyme we should mention *alliteration* — this is the practice of using groups of words which have the same *first* letters!

Finally, there is free verse. This is verse where the metre is not obvious, or is very complicated. Much modern poetry is written in free verse, and much of it is not really verse at all, because the people writing it do not understand that you must have metre or rhythm. It may be a very complicated metre, but it has to be there. *Good* free verse is very hard to write.

(a) Here are some lines of poetry written as if they were prose. Write them out correctly as verse (remembering to start each new line with a capital letter.) In each case you have been told how many lines of verse are contained in what you have been given. (15)

   (1) The earth was green, the sky was blue: I saw and heard one sunny morn a skylark hang between the two, a singing speck above the corn. (4 lines)

   (2) Under the wide and starry sky, dig the grave and let me lie. Glad did I live and gladly die, and I laid me down with a will. (4 lines)

   (3) In summertime on Bredon the bells they sound so clear; round both the shires they ring them in steeples far and near; a happy sound to hear. (5 lines)

   (4) And now the sun had stretched out all the hills, and now was dropped into the western bay; at last he rose, and twitched his mantle blue: tomorrow to fresh woods and pastures new. (4 lines)

   (5) This royal throne of kings, this sceptred isle, this earth of majesty, this seat of Mars, this other Eden, demi-paradise; this fortress built by nature for herself against infection and the hand of war . . . (5 lines)

(b) Now try to *scan* the verses you have written out in their correct form for (a). Remember that this involves dividing each line into the poetic feet, and marking the long and short syllables. Here are some clues to help you with each one:—

   (1) You have only one sort of foot to worry about here: ∪— (the iambus).

   (2) This is harder. The first three lines have feet of the —∪ and—∪∪ sort; the last line of the ∪— and ∪∪— sort. There are also three lines which end with a single long syllable.

   (3) This is rather easier again, with ∪— predominating; but there are two lines that have a single odd syllable at the end again!

   (4) This is easier still; entirely ∪— .

   (5) This is blank verse, — so there are no rhymes. But it has a perfect unvaried rhythm, with each line exactly the same, — so you should be able to work out the metre for yourself! (30)

(c) In this exercise, you are given two lines of verse, to which you have to add two further lines of your own. In both cases you have to write rhyming verse!

However, you are given considerable assistance with the metre you should use, so that what you write does fit with what is already there, and you are also helped with some suggested rhymes. It is still quite hard, though!

   (1)   Across the meadows and the woods
               Whispers the stealthy breeze.........

Line 3 —   ∪—|∪—|∪—|∪—|
Line 4 —   ∪—|∪—|∪—|or —∪|—∪|—|
Line 4 has to end with a rhyme for *breeze*. Some possibilities are:— trees, seas, ease, flees, frees, seize. (5)

   (2)   Our way lies through the Mountains of Despair
           The Vales of Sorrow, and the caverns where.........

Lines 3 and 4 — ∪—|∪—|∪—|∪—|∪—|

You have to write two lines, each with five poetic feet, and the two lines must rhyme with each other.

Notice that you have to carry on the sense from *where*...... (Perhaps you might go on to mention some other unpleasant abstractions similar to *Despair* and *Sorrow* which inhabit these caverns!) (5)

(d) For each of the following write four lines of verse — or more if you prefer — incorporating the pairs of rhymes you are given. You can use the rhymes where you think they fit best, and you can include other rhymes too if you wish.

   (1) *star* and *far*.   (2) *grey* and *away*.   (3) *stone* and *alone*. (15)

(e) Write down all the examples of *alliteration* you can find in the following:—

          That is a land of lost content,
            I see it shining plain,
         The happy highways where I went
           And cannot come again. (10)

FACTSHEET TWENTY-SEVEN

STYLE (1)

In poetry as well as prose, the quality of what you write will depend on the way you write it. The way you write things is your *style*. A great deal of this book has been aimed at helping you to improve your style. Now, at the end of the book, we need to sum up some of those points. Good style comes down to three essential qualities:— CLARITY, EFFECTIVENESS and VARIETY. On this Factsheet we will look at CLARITY.

Clarity means simply *being clear*. There is not much point in writing anything at all, if your reader cannot understand what you are going on about. There are various enemies of clarity, the first of which is VERBOSITY.

Verbosity is probably the biggest threat when you are writing descriptive essays. It is the tendency to go on and on saying the same thing with slightly different words. Obviously there are many occasions when you do want to use a variety of similar descriptive words and phrases to build up an atmosphere, create an effect, or paint a vivid scene. It is important, though, to make sure that every word or phrase you use does really add something. If it does not, then do without it. In particular, avoid heaps of adjectives piled together.

(For example: "It was a huge and massive arena, of vast size and circumference." We have three adjectives here meaning *very large*, — and does *size* mean anything different from *circumference* in this case?)

When you are writing precise explanations, in factual essays or in letters, the chief thing to avoid is probably AMBIGUITY. You do not want to write sentences that have more than one possible meaning or interpretation. Ambiguity usually arises from careless organization of your sentences — in particular from putting things in the wrong order — or from poor punctuation. For example, there is the question on a form: "Where were you wounded?" — Does it want you to reply "In the arm", or "In the Falklands"? The question is ambiguous.

Similar is the sentence: "I have requested a permit to transport the cattle by post." Unless the writer intends to use very large envelopes, he must mean: "I have requested by post a permit to transport the cattle."

The next thing to avoid, especially in ordinary narrative and descriptive writing, is *jargon*. JARGON is the special language of science and technology, and of some trades and professions. (The worst and most unintelligible jargon, by the way, is employed by people who work in education.)

If you have to use a technical term, explain what it means:— your reader may be less learned in nuclear physics or prosody ('the art of writing poetry') than you are! If you are writing a technical explanation of something, then you will have to use the technical terms: but if you are writing it for ordinary people you will still need to explain those terms. (Notice that SLANG is a species of jargon:— do not use it!)

OFFICIALESE and COMMERCIALESE are humorous words invented for the sort of language preferred by people who write business and commercial letters. The unfortunate thing is that you are more likely to get a useful response from an official department by writing:

"I would beg to remind you of my communication in re compensation payments" than by writing "Please answer my letter about my compensation".

Officialese is full of verbosity. It never uses one word where five would do. So it says 'at this moment in time' when it means 'now' and 'It is of importance to bear in mind the following' when it means 'Please remember'. You may not be able to fight the system when you are writing to some people . . . . but do avoid this sort of drivel when you are writing essays.

The worst style of all is found in JOURNALESE, the language employed by newspapers. Its grammar is often poor. It often uses slang. It concentrates on producing clever phrases — though these are often clichés — instead of explanations. In its headlines (where the objective is both to save space and catch the eye) it reduces the language to the brink of nonsense. (What does 'Cops probe council claims row' mean?)

As well as reading this indiscriminate mixture of slang, jargon and journalese in the newspapers, you can hear its spoken form on television and radio programmes, especially news, current affairs and 'consumer' programmes.

If you are ever told to write a newspaper report, or if you want to *be* a journalist, you will need to do the opposite of much of what you have been taught in this book — though Factsheet Three, on 'Slant', will help you.

These are some of the things to try to avoid in your writing. There are other positive actions you can take.

Firstly, get the grammar, spelling and punctuation right. (There are other books in this series to assist you with these items!)

Secondly, think about what you are saying as you write. Make sure it makes sense as you go along. Make it a rule that you always read through your compositions when you finish them. (You may find it particularly useful to read them aloud!) This way you will pick up silly mistakes. Even in exams, if you can spare the time to do this, it is worth it.

Finally, PLAN your essay in advance. You may be fed up with hearing this, but it is very important. If you know in advance what you intend to say, you are more likely to say it clearly, precisely, and concisely.

(a) Rewrite this verbose passage, retaining only those adverbs, adjectives, and even in some cases nouns and verbs, which are actually necessary to the meaning or add something to the description. You can reorganize the structure in the process if you wish.

> High above them, dwarfing them with their impossible immensity, reared the Cyclopean columns of that unutterably vast and unearthly temple. There, antique, gargantuan pillars stood crumbling with the immense weight of untold, immemorial years. There, time-stained primeval porticos, unknowably ancient before the Flood, daunting in their enormity, were hung about with the primordial lichens of countless, interminable aeons, and intertwined with the primitive ferns of antediluvian ages, long forgotten.

It might well be worth glancing back at Factsheet Nine on the use of the 'Adjective-Vacuum' in dealing with this passage. You will also need a dictionary, — which will reveal that a remarkable number of the words used mean either 'old' or 'big'. . . . . . .   (20)

(b) Here are two pieces of officialese (1) and commercialese (2). Once again, your job is to rewrite them in plain English, so that it is possible to understand what on earth they mean. — Be ruthless!

  (1)   In the event of the implementation of the current regulations on the basis of an excessively strict interpretation of the provisions laid down, it is conceded that some measure of hardship to those to whom the said regulations may be applied might be anticipated.   (5)

  (2)   Failure to engage in high-risk ventures of a speculative character will result in a consequent failure to achieve the substantial rewards indicated by the very nature of such schemes.   (5)

  It is in fact possible to reduce number (2) to a proverb — four words long! See if you can think of it.

(c) Imagine you are a senior official in a local government department. You are writing a memo giving some instructions to your staff. What you really want to say is this:—

  (i)   There have been too many complaints from people about inefficiency in the Department.
  (ii)   Too many of these complaints have reached me.
  (iii)   It is the job of junior officials to fob people off with excuses.
  (iv)   The quality of these excuses needs to be improved.
  (v)   Make sure I have a quiet life — or you certainly will not have one.

Now you cannot of course tell the truth in plain language like this. So try to compose your version of the memorandum in 'officialese'. Your object is still to convey the same message of course, but for once you can be as verbose and pompous as you like.   (20)

(d) The following sentences are ambiguous. — Rewrite them (or at least revise their punctuation) so that they can have only one meaning.

  (1)   Nothing is better than new improved Whizzo.
  (2)   An official statement was made on the number of muggings in the House of Commons yesterday.
  (3)   We would not wish to accept responsibility for supplying such a large area with all its attendant difficulties.
  (4)   People in the South keep their teeth longer than people in the North.
  (5)   If the baby does not thrive on raw milk, boil it.   (10)

(e) Imagine you are a journalist working for a major British newspaper. You have to report a story. The truth of the matter, in short, is as follows:—

> A large, old house is to be demolished by a developer.
> The developer claims it is in a dangerous condition.
> The proposal is to build a multi-storey car-park on the site.
> There is no doubt that a car park is needed.
> The house has, however, been occupied by squatters.
> They belong to the 'Save Our Heritage Organization'.
> They say the house is of historical interest and worth saving.
> They also say that houses are more important than car-parks.

  (1)   Write the story in such a way that you support the developer. You can attack the squatters in any way whatsoever. You do not of course have to rely on the facts of the matter; you can make up any additional 'colour' you like. (No doubt the squatters are long-haired, drug-taking layabouts!)   (15)

  (2)   Now write the story supporting the squatters. (Now of course the property-developer is a money-grubbing, bloated capitalist!)   (15)

In each case write your own headline in no more than five words.

FACTSHEET TWENTY-EIGHT

STYLE (2)

The second essential for good style is EFFECTIVENESS. This is about using the right words for the right sense. All the writing you do is to some purpose. You are trying to narrate a series of events, to describe a scene, to explain something, to discuss a particular point, to give some impression, or create a particular effect. You need to use the words and phrases that serve your purpose best. We will begin by looking at some of the effects or impressions you might want to create.

Perhaps the hardest effect to achieve is, surprisingly enough, HUMOUR. If you set out to try to write humorously, you will probably fail. It is particularly inadvisable to try to tell jokes! If you have a genuinely funny series of events to relate, do so without comment. If your writing is clear and vivid, the humour will be apparent to your reader.

SATIRE, where you hold a person or his opinions up to ridicule, has been called 'the lowest form of wit'. It is also very hard to do well, as you can see by watching satirical television programmes. IRONY is a rather more clever form of wit, where you poke fun at someone by saying one thing about him, but suggesting the opposite. It is even harder to do than satire. In exams in particular, it is best not to employ humour; the examiner may think you are trying to be funny . . .

Just as difficult to do is PATHOS. This is when you are trying to make your reader feel sad about, or at least sympathetic towards, one of your characters. Once again, the best way to do it is to describe the 'sad scene' clearly and directly, using simple words. Do not pile on the adjectives. Do not tell your readers how terribly sad it all is. Do not go over the top. If you do, your pathos will rapidly become pathetic. Look at these two examples:—

(1) "She looked down at the grave. Her vision blurred for a moment, but she steadied herself. She had decided that she would not weep. She took the handful of earth, and threw it, rattling on to the coffin, the grains like the scattered years of his life. All gone now, all lost."

(2) "The poor, sad, little girl stood by the graveside. Tears trickled down her nose from her large brown eyes, as she cuddled her old, tattered teddy bear. Now there was no-one to protect her in the cruel world, and she would have to go to the orphanage."

The second one does not work so well because it goes over the top — and has too many clichés. In order to make your reader feel sympathy for your characters, you need to make a good job of describing those characters. If they seem real, then the reader will be sorry for them when they are unhappy, and afraid for them when they are in danger.

The same rule applies when you are trying to achieve numerous effects. If you are trying to create an atmosphere, of SUSPENSE, the description of the echoing steps in the empty room above, the creaking door, the sudden extinguishing of the candle, all will work far better if your reader can identify with the hero, shivering in terror behind the curtains. If you have not made a good job of describing that hero, in making him into a real person, then the things that happen to him will not seem quite so important, or even interesting.

Characterization is very important, but with the skilful use of words you can give a scene, a place, a building a 'character' of its own. That is the other sense behind the phrase 'bringing a scene alive'.

So use words carefully. Choose the right word, and always think about the impression you are trying to give, the atmosphere you want to create. Even in a purely factual essay you want to give one impression — that you know what you are talking about, and can adopt the style (accurate, precise, but simple and straightforward) which best fits that aim.

So finally we come to VARIETY. When you write you want to make your writing as interesting, entertaining and lively as you can, not only for your reader, but for your own satisfaction.

This book began with the statement 'Variety is the spice of life'. You now know enough to label this as a cliché. But it still has a meaning. A *spice* is what adds flavour to food that might otherwise be tasteless. That is what you are doing to your writing when you make variety one of its most important ingredients.

There are many sorts of variety. You can vary sentence length, and the form of sentences you use. You can employ different manners of description, varying subordinate clauses with descriptive phrases and both of them with simple adjectives and adverbs. You can mix narrative with description, and mix both with explanation. In telling a story you can, and should, include characterization; you can set the scene, and create atmosphere. You can vary your choice of words, always searching for the most suitable one. You can use similes and metaphors.

In all of these things your aim is to make something that is new and original, and yours. Writing essays, stories and compositions is not just another task, like doing an exercise or solving a problem. It is *you* creating something.

(a) Write a description of the following sequence of events:—

A man is hauling a bucket up the side of a building on a pulley.
Someone puts some bricks in it at the top.
The weight of the bucket pulls the man up, as it goes down.
On the way down it hits him, and he goes on to the top.
Meanwhile, the bucket reaches the bottom, and someone empties the bricks.
Up goes the bucket and down comes the man.
On the way it hits him again.
He lands heavily on the ground and lets go of the rope.
The bucket falls from the top and lands on his head.

The effect you are trying to achieve in telling this little story is *humour*. You really should be able to make this story funny, as it is used very successfully by a professional comedian. Remember, it's the way you tell it that counts . . .

(20)

(b) Write a description of a boy or girl who is *afraid*. Do not put him or her into an unusual or unlikely situation. Haunted houses or remote chasms amidst uncharted jungles are not allowed. Stick to real life. If you can, write from your own experience.

You need to start by outlining the situation — perhaps your character has become lost in a strange town, or is in trouble for some sort of wrongdoing. Then you need to make your character real. We need to know what he or she is thinking and feeling; we need to know what sort of person he or she is. If you succeed, not only will your character really appear to be afraid, but your reader will be afraid with him — and for him.

(20)

(c) Write a description of an old house, just before it is pulled down. Try to give the house a 'feeling' or even a 'character' of its own. Suggest age and decay, but also 'weariness', and perhaps 'resignation'. Use the device of the house's 'memories' to suggest happy days gone by. Then try to contrast these with present 'sadness'. Think carefully about this before you start to write, and try to find other ways you can almost make the house 'live'.   (20)

(d) Write a piece in which your aim is to build up suspense. Your passage should be divided into two sections (which may each be a paragraph, or may be longer if you wish.) The first part should set the scene and tell the reader about your characters. You are to have two or more characters in the story. — The second part should concentrate on the build up of the suspense, through whatever sequence of events you choose. The Factsheet will give you an idea of how to go about it. This time you may use the boring old haunted house if you really cannot think of any other setting.

(20)

(e) Select one of the following titles, and write a precise, factual description of the process, designed to explain it to someone who has never done it before. — So make sure that it is a process you do know how to carry out yourself. Do not use technical words, unless you explain them. Be as clear as you possibly can. Remember to describe accurately the things that are involved, but do not include unnecessary information. Also, since you are giving directions, try to write in a friendly and helpful style — like this book . . .

(1)   Making a Cake   (2)   Using a Video-Recorder   (3)   Mending a Bicycle Puncture

(4)   Wiring a Plug   (5)   Taking a Photograph   (6)   Dyeing Your Hair

You may write as little or as much as you feel is necessary for the topic you choose.

(20)

(f) Make a list of ten different ways you can add variety to your writing. This is not particularly difficult since several ways are mentioned in the Factsheet. Your second task, however, is to write a paragraph in which you use every single one of the ten methods you have listed. — You may make it a rather long paragraph if you wish. It may be on any topic you wish, but it would probably be sensible to make it a mixture of narrative and description, since that is itself one of the best ways of ensuring variety. As you are writing, think about your style. If you *try* to write well, you will stand a better chance of succeeding in doing just that.

(10) + (20)

(g) Write an essay.
You may select any title. Choose the form of essay you are best at. You now know all the 'tricks of the trade'. Make a real effort to put them to the best possible use. If you use the skills you have learnt, you cannot fail to write a decent essay. You may not have people flocking to your door for the film rights — but you will almost certainly satisfy the examiners for the English paper!

(40)

Factsheets One to Seven

(a) For each of these verbs give three synonyms, and three antonyms.

    (1) increase   (2) give   (3) waste   (4) lose   (5) hope

(15)

(b) Arrange these two sets of synonyms in order of force or intensity. Start with the least or weakest.

| (1) | execration | dislike | loathing | hatred | hostility |
| (2) | infatuation | devotion | liking | love | fondness |

(5)

(c) In the following list of twenty words there are four sets of synonyms. Each set has five words in it. Write out the synonyms in four separate lists.

diagram	sickly	outline	ask	enquire
unhealthy	examine	unconscious	asleep	ailing
drawing	blueprint	unwell	sketch	comatose
interrogate	question	insensible	ill	slumbering

(20)

(d) This passage of description is not very informative. Rewrite it using more precise words. The words you definitely need to replace are printed in italics. You may also want to make other changes in the layout or sentence structure. Your aim is to convey more information.

> Auntie's house is very *nice*. It has a *big* garden with *lots of pretty* flowers. Inside there are seven *good* rooms, all with *delightful* views. There is a *lovely* carpet in the sitting room, and *beautiful* wallpaper too. The house is also in a *good* area, and the neighbours are very *pleasant*.

(20)

(e) Rewrite these sentences in such a way that you reverse their slant. Your aim is to say much the same thing, but to give the opposite impression to that conveyed. You will not need to change all the words, of course, but you need to think carefully about which ones can usefully be altered, — and about the synonyms to be employed. You may change the structure and order of the sentence if it is necesary.

    (1)   We have received reports of a terrorist raid on the home of the president.   (8)

    (2)   The death penalty is no more than legalized vengeance.   (4)

    (3)   The property is a compact period residence, with many striking original features still in situ.   (8)

(20)

(f) Write out the following passage, inserting appropriate similes in the spaces. Try to be original in your choice of comparisons. You may use one word or several in each case.

> As slow as ...., as quiet as ...., the creature stirred its massive bulk. Its great mass floated like .... in the clinging swamp. Its eyes, as sharp as ...., glinted like .... above the murky surface. The creature saw its prey, waiting for it there like ...., as heedless as .... They were unaware of the sudden silence that had fallen like .... over the scene. They laughed and played as if ....
> But they were mere insects, already in the spider's web, their fate as sure as ....

(20)

(g) Explain why the words underlined in each of the following sentences are metaphorical. Try to say what they mean when they are used in these special ways.

    (1)   Finally her anger goaded her into action.

    (2)   He has left behind him a trail of disasters.

    (3)   His hungry eyes bored into me.

    (4)   In the light of these revelations, I have decided to stand down.

    (5)   Angry seas lashed the jagged rocks.

    (6)   The poison of her hatred boiled inside her.

    (7)   The biting frost turned my fingers into icicles.

    (8)   Let us kindle a beacon of hope amidst this landscape of despair.

    (9)   You may think he is quite a lion, my dear, but I think he is a young cub.

    (10)   I have fire in my heart; you have water in your veins.

    (11)   The razor of his wit cuts no ice with me.

(40)

Factsheets Eight to Thirteen

(a) In the following sentences you have two tasks:—
    (i)   Where there is an asterisk (*) insert a suitable adjective or adverb.   (10)
    (ii)   Try to replace every word in italics with a better synonym.   (10)
    Write out each sentence incorporating the changes you have made.

    (1)   Amidst the *quiet* of that * *cave* came the * sound of water dropping * at some * distance into a * *hole*.
    (2)   There was a * *fire burning* in the * *building* when we arrived.
    (3)   Lisa was * awoken from her sleep by the * *sound* of the bell.
    (4)   We could see the * mountains now, their *tops covered in* snow, glittering in the *light*. (N.B. Replace *tops* as well as *covered in*.)

(b) In the following short passage there are forty adjectives and adverbs.
    (1)   Write out the passage as it stands, and underline all the adverbs and adjectives.   (20)
    (2)   Now go over the passage with an 'Adjective-Vacuum' (as usual, the sort that removes unnecessary adverbs as well). Reduce the number of adjectives and adverbs combined by half. Try to remove the ones that are unnecessary, and keep those that add to the effectiveness of the description.   (20)

> The wild and fiercely surging seas smashed cruel and cold ceaselessly against the iron-hard, grim, grey rocks beneath the sheer, steep cliff. White, flying, tiny specks of salty, briny spray rose in flowery, bushy fountains, momentary and transient in their shivering, shimmering splendour, then fell suddenly, swiftly, down into the all-embracing, all-devouring, eternal oblivion of the ever-flowing, never-changing ocean. High above, the calling, screaming gulls whirled in a furious and frenetic dance to the dour, deep Sea-God down below.

(c) Write out the following sentences, inserting a clause or phrase to modify the verbs in italics. You may add more than one clause and/or phrase if you wish, but do not make the sentences too unwieldy. The object of the exercise is to add more detail to the sentences and improve their descriptive content.
(For example:— 'She *shouted* the instructions' could become 'She shouted the instructions in a high and piercing voice'.)

    (1)   She *sprang* from the quayside on to the deck.
    (2)   He *laughed* at me, then turned on his heel and left.
    (3)   In the empty room, our voices *echoed*.
    (4)   The starlight *shone* through the open curtains.
    (5)   Sandie *was checking* the accounts.   (20)

(d) This is much the same. Insert an adjectival phrase or clause to qualify the nouns in italics.
    (1)   The *detective* was waiting on the corner of the street.
    (2)   The *stairs* were in darkness.
    (3)   Are you absolutely certain that this is the *house*.
    (4)   The *silence* after that remark was deafening.
    (5)   We are now confronted with a very difficult *decision*.   (20)

(e) Combine the sentences in each of the following into a single sentence. You may use any methods. Try to produce a clear, well-constructed sentence as the result.
    (1)   This is the path. We have to take it. It is steep and dangerous. It leads to the top of the cliff. There we will find the cabin.
    (2)   The teacher told her to read the book. She went out and bought it. She found it very boring. It was also hard to understand.
    (3)   It was very cold. We could not go out. We decided to play in my bedroom. Then we broke the window. It was rather cold inside now.
    (4)   We were looking for the hotel. It was supposed to be on a hill. We knew it was at a crossroads. Night was drawing on. The fog had started to come down. We were lost.
    (5)   Steve flew over the handlebars. He landed in a holly bush. He was crying loudly. He was not crying because of the holly. The bicycle's wheel was bent. It was his father's bicycle. That was why he was crying.   (30)

Factsheets Fourteen to Twenty-One

(a)   Here is a list of essay titles, or instructions for essays. Read through them carefully, and think about them, then answer the questions that follow:—

(i)   *The Fun of the Fair.*   (iv)   *Illusions.*
(ii)   *Gifts.*   (v)   *The Day the Roof Fell Down.*
(iii)   *Stowaways.*   (vi)   *Broken Memories.*
(vii)   *Write an essay beginning with the words:—*
    "I knocked confidently on the door, little suspecting what awaited me within".
(viii)   *Imagine you are a church clock looking down on the scene below. Tell the story of your years.*
(ix)   *You are in a public place, perhaps waiting for someone. It is very busy, and many people are hurrying by. Write an essay entitled: 'Faces in a Crowd'.*
(x)   *This is the third verse of a poem entitled 'The Highwayman', by Alfred Noyes. Read it carefully, then write an essay based on any or all of the ideas and images contained in the verse. You may use the same title, or a different one.*

> *Over the cobbles he clattered and clashed in the dark inn-yard,*
> *And he tapped with his whip on the shutters, but all was locked and barred;*
> *He whistled a tune to the window, and who should be waiting there*
> *But the landlord's black-eyed daughter,*
>   *Bess, the landlord's daughter,*
> *Plaiting a dark red love-knot into her long black hair.*

(1)   For each of the above titles, say whether you think the title is best suited to a largely narrative essay, or to a mainly descriptive essay, or to an essay where the two sorts of writing are both required equally. Try to explain why you have classified the titles in the way you have.   (30)

(2)   Do an essay plan for each title. This means that you first need to think of the *theme* or *plot* of your story, and note it down in a few sentences or phrases. Then you need to set out the basic structure, planning paragraph by paragraph, noting the key events in each. Next to each paragraph 'heading' you also need to jot down reminders of other elements that you want to include.   (40)

(3)   Write an interesting, striking, or original *opening* for each of the essays. Try not to write more than two or three sentences (or only one if it is particularly good).   (30)

(4)   Write an *ending* for each of the essays. Once again, only write the last two or three sentences — unless your ending is quite complicated. It would be sensible to check back to Factsheet Eighteen before you do this, as writing endings is one of the most difficult parts of writing an essay.   (30)

(5)   For each of the endings you have written for question (4), classify it. — Say what type of ending it is, or explain how it combines several types of ending.   (10)

(b)   Here is an essay plan, for an essay entitled: *The Market*. Your job is to write the essay. Try to employ all your narrative and descriptive skills. (Some of the paragraphs may stretch into two.)   (40)

Para. 1. Historical perspective:— Scenes of past market days there	Describe what it was like; trading in the Middle Ages; cattle droves later on. Start with a vivid account of one of these.
Para. 2. Describe the scene *now* in a broad sweep.	The stalls and their awnings, the goods on display, the throng of people, the buildings around the square.
Para. 3. Pick out a few aspects for more detailed description; use the *senses* for variations.	The fishmonger's stall; the children's roundabout; the busker.
Para. 4. Scenes and characters.	An old man selling toys; a child trying to persuade his mother to buy one; a tradesman arguing with a housewife.
Para. 5. A narrative interlude:— the chase.	A youth tries to steal something. His escape!
Para. 6. Start to wind down the excitement. The 'dying fall' ending.	The characters talk about the events. Day wears on into evening. Packing up. Nightfall. The evening scene.

Factsheets Twenty-Two to Twenty-Eight

(a)   Here are the instructions supplied for some essays. Read them carefully, then for each one write an essay plan. Check Factsheets Twenty-Two, Twenty-Three and Twenty-Four on how to do essays of this sort, and draw up your plans accordingly. In the 'Discuss. . .' type of essays (and the review) remember that your plan must allow for both sides of the argument. Also remember what you have learnt about the importance of clarity and accuracy — particularly in the 'explanation' essays. — Your essay will not be clear if your plan is not clear.   (30)

(1)   *All girls should go to mixed schools: all boys should go to single-sex schools. Discuss.*
      (*Note:*— Do not dwell on the obvious impossibility of the proposition; the person who originally set the title intended the joke; concentrate on whether the proposition would be correct if it were possible.)

(2)   *Describe television to a Martian. He has no idea of it whatsoever, as Martians communicate over distances by entirely different means, but he is highly intelligent and speaks good English.*

(3)   *There would be less crime if the courts were allowed to impose far more severe penalties on criminals. — Do you agree?*
      (Be careful to make sure you understand exactly what the question means. Also remember that in your plan you must provide for both sides of the case, and whether you agree or not you must support your opinion fully with evidence and argument.)

(4)   *Preparing a three-course meal for a dinner party.*
      (This is intended to be an 'explanation' essay. Do not try to twist it into a narrative.)

(5)   *Imagine you are a salesman for a major company. (Its product can be anything you wish.) You are on a promotional trip to the Far East, visiting your company's existing customers to sort out any problems they have with your product and to try to increase your sales to them; you are also trying to obtain new orders from new customers. Write a letter to your managing director, explaining how you have gone about your task, what success you have had, and what problems you have encountered.*
      (Notice that this is a good example of a situation where it is essential to plan a letter in advance, because it needs to be lengthy and quite complicated.)

(6)   *Write a review of a novel or short story you have read recently. Explain what, in your opinion, made it a successful (or unsuccessful) work of fiction.*

(b)   *Read this complete poem ('Ozymandias' by Percy Bysshe Shelley), and then answer the questions.*

> I met a traveller from an antique land
> Who said: Two vast and trunkless legs of stone
> Stand in the desert. Near them on the sand,
> Half sunk, a shattered visage lies, whose frown,
> And wrinkled lip, and sneer of cold command,
> Tell that its sculptor well those passions read
> Which yet survive, stamped on these lifeless things,
> The hand that mocked them and the heart that fed;
> And on the pedestal these words appear:
>   'My name is Ozymandias, king of kings:
>   Look on my works, ye mighty, and despair!'
> Nothing beside remains. Round the decay
> Of that colossal wreck, boundless and bare
> The lone and level sands stretch far away.

(1)   Write out the first six lines to show the scansion.   (30)

(2)   Write a poem of your own, using the same metre (including the same line length) as the first two lines of the above poem. Take the theme for your poem from any aspect of the poem by Shelley, or any idea suggested to you by it. Make sure you do at least a rough plan before you start to write.   (30)

(3)   Write a summary of the poem *Ozymandias* in *not more than* fifty words. You must decide what is essential and what can be left out. Think carefully!   (20)

(4)   Imagine *you* are Ozymandias, king of kings (or queen of queens, if you are a girl!) Write an essay about some aspect of your life. Your account may be a narrative, or descriptive, or an explanation. Whatever you write you have two underlying tasks: firstly, to set the scene of Ozymandias's world; secondly to characterize *yourself* as Ozymandias . . . . Good luck!   (40)

ESSAY TITLES

A list of the essay titles and topics used or mentioned in this book.

1. An Unexpected Meeting
2. Night Train
3. The Practical Joke
4. A Day of Disasters
5. Appointment with Danger
6. A Horse's Tale
7. Suddenly I Found Myself Invisible
8. A Journey I Would Rather Forget
9. The Door I Was Told Not To Open
10. Autumn Leaves
11. A Day to Remember
12. A Terrible Disappointment
13. My Favourite Lessons
14. The Face at the Window
15. Looking After Little Brother Sammy
16. Moving House
17. Inside the Television
18. Collecting as a Hobby
19. The Statue that Spoke
20. My Home Town
21. A Mistake on the Overnight Sleeper
22. A Holiday that Went Wrong
23. Trouble in the Street
24. On the Wrong Track
25. And Then There Was One . . .
26. An Interesting Journey
27. The Race
28. The Haunted House
29. An Unexpected Encounter
30. No Hiding Place
31. Treasure Island
32. The Eventful Day
33. Flight to Nowhere
34. The Mysterious Letter
35. What My Little Sister Did
36. Never Believe What You hear
37. In a Hurry
38. Trapped
39. Flight to Freedom
40. The Secret Room
41. Shipwreck
42. Chance Encounter
43. Ever Decreasing Circles
44. The Happy Wanderers
45. Lost in the Forest
46. All at Sea
47. A Wish Come True
48. Enemies
49. The Man Who Never Came
50. Fire on the Hilltop
51. Some Day I Will Return
52. The New Job
53. The Chimney Sweep
54. Aunts and Uncles
55. Teachers I Have Known
56. Passers-By
57. My Best Friend
58. The Funniest Person I Ever Met
59. The Boss
60. My Boyfriend *or* My Girlfriend
61. People Who Live On My Street
62. The Girl (or Boy) with the Bobble Hat
63. Shop Windows
64. On the Beach
65. My Favourite Possessions
66. The Docks
67. Pictures in the Fire
68. The Old Oak Tree
69. Village Fields
70. Woodland Creatures
71. The Old Church
72. My Family
73. A Visit to the Fairground
74. My Birthday
75. A School Day
76. An Outing in the Park
77. What I did on my Holidays
78. Autumn Days
79. The Seashore
80. A Day at the Beach

81. The Toy Shop: write a story about what you would see on a visit to a toy shop.
82. Discuss the Advantages and Disadvantages of Having a Prefect System at School.
83. Was it a Mistake to Abolish the Death Penalty for Murder?
84. Describe the Job of *either* an Airline Pilot *or* a Fashion Designer.
85. Imagine you are a Glass Marble. Describe your Life and Adventures.
86. The Advantages of Learning Science at School.
87. My Home: write a description of the house or flat where you live and the people you share it with.
88. A Day that Changed my Life.
89. Imagine you are a toy in a toy cupboard. Describe your experiences and adventures.
90. Imagine you are a chess piece. Write a story about your life and adventures.
91. Write a composition beginning with the words: "Suddenly I found myself growing . . ."
92. And that Taught us Never to Write on Walls.
93. A Narrow Escape — A Story Told by a Mouse.
94. Imagine you are sitting in a bus or train. Describe your fellow passengers.
95. The Person Who Has Influenced Me Most.
96. Discuss the advantages of learning a foreign language.

97. Cruel sports should be banned. Do you agree?
98. Are private schools better than state schools?
99. The advantages and disadvantages of boarding schools.
100. Was it a mistake to abolish corporal punishment in schools?
101. Write a composition beginning: "The table seemed larger, and the chair too! My feet weren't touching the floor any more. My clothes were hanging loosely on me . . ."
102. Write a composition based on these lines of poetry, or the ideas and images contained in them:—
    "Day after day, day after day,
      We stuck, nor breath nor motion;
      As idle as a painted ship
      Upon a painted ocean."
103. Write an essay which begins with the words: "I had just sat down on the park bench. Tom had taken Patch off for a run among the trees. Baby John was feeding the ducks, safe in the care of Annie. Now I could have a rest . . ."
104. You and a friend, or some friends, are on holiday near an old and partly-ruined house. You decide to explore it. Write a story about your adventures in the house.
105. Myself When Young. (Describe what you were like as a small child; you may decide which age to pick — or you may survey yourself at several ages, as you grew older.)
106. My Home Town. Write a description of the town, district or village where you live.
107. Describe the nature of the work done by a person in any one job, trade or profession of your choice.
108. Democracy is a bad form of government, but all the other forms are much worse. Discuss.
109. Write an essay beginning with the words: "I knocked confidently on the door, little suspecting what awaited me within . . ."
110. Imagine you are a church clock looking down on the scene below. Tell the story of your years.
111. You are in a public place, perhaps waiting for someone. It is very busy, and many people are hurrying by. Write an essay entitled: Faces in a Crowd.
112. This is the third verse of a poem entitled 'The Highwayman', by Alfred Noyes. Read it carefully, then write an essay based on any or all of the ideas and images contained in the verse. You may use the same title or a different one.
    "Over the cobbles he clattered and clashed in the dark inn-yard,
      And he tapped with his whip on the shutters, but all was locked and barred;
      He whistled a tune to the window, and who should be waiting there
      But the landlord's black-eyed daughter,
        Bess, the landlord's daughter,
      Plaiting a dark red love-knot into her long black hair."
113. All girls should go to mixed schools; all boys should go to single-sex schools. Discuss.
114. Describe television to a Martian. He has no idea of it whatsoever, as Martians communicate over distances by entirely different means, but he is highly intelligent, and speaks good English.
115. There would be less crime if the courts were allowed to impose far more severe penalties on criminals. Do you agree?
116. Preparing a three-course meal for a dinner party.
117. Christmas Presents
118. He Was Certainly a curious Fellow . . .
119. Ill In Bed
120. A Railway Journey
121. The Market Place
122. Model-Making as a Hobby
123. Ballet
124. The Red Cross Organization
125. The Rules of Football
126. How to Drive a Car
127. Horse Riding
128. Spooks are Spoofs. — Discuss
129. Should there be School Uniforms?
130. The Death Penalty: Right or Wrong?
131. Women in Politics
132. Nuclear Disarmament
133. The Loch Ness Monster
134. Prison Reform
135. My Kind of Music
136. How to be Happy
137. Making a Cake
138. Wiring a Plug
139. Using a Video-Recorder
140. Taking a Photograph
141. Mending a Bicycle Puncture
142. Dyeing Your hair
143. The Fun of the Fair
144. Stowaways
145. Illusions
146. The Day the Roof Fell Down
147. Broken Memories
148. Gifts

In addition to the above titles, there are essays requiring a review of a book, film, etc. There are also many sorts of letter — personal, official, business etc.

Many of the titles given can be used as well for verse as for prose.

INDEX